Uncle Arthur's
BEDTIME
STORIES
Volume Four

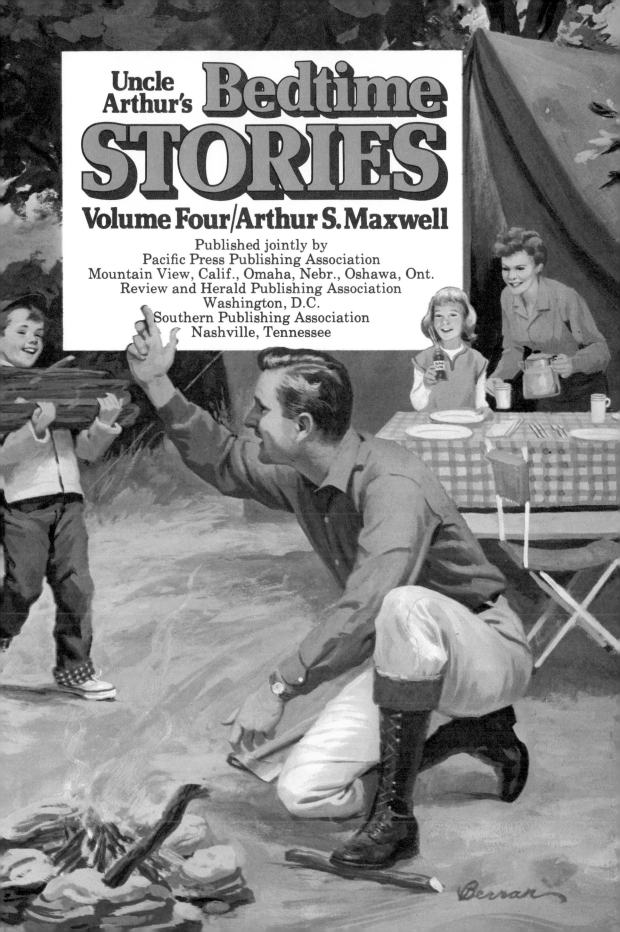

Uncle Arthur's Bedtime STORIES

Volume Four/Arthur S. Maxwell

Published jointly by
Pacific Press Publishing Association
Mountain View, Calif., Omaha, Nebr., Oshawa, Ont.
Review and Herald Publishing Association
Washington, D.C.
Southern Publishing Association
Nashville, Tennessee

Contents

5

◄ Color Photo by J. Byron Logan

6

Lesson Index

Artists participating in the illustration of this volume are: Harry Anderson, Harry Baerg, Robert Berran, Jennie Brownscombe, Fred Collins, Kreigh Collins, William Dolwick, John Gourley, Russ Harlan, William Heaslip, William Hutchinson, Manning de V. Lee, Donald Muth, Vernon Nye, B. Plockhorst, Peter Rennings, and Jack White. Cover by John Steel.

STORY **1**

Mother's Hands

JUST WHEN IT HAPPENED I do not know. Maybe fifty years ago, maybe a hundred. It really doesn't matter. The story was old when I was a boy and that's quite some time ago now. I tell it again because you will love it, too.

A sweet young mother, having laid her baby girl to sleep in her cradle, went down the street to visit a neighbor. She had often left her baby before, just for a few minutes, and there had been no trouble; so she had no doubt that all would be well now.

Arriving at the neighbor's house, she began to chat about this and that, but was suddenly interrupted by a sound that always sent a chill through her, the city fire alarm.

"Don't worry," said the neighbor. "Most likely it's only a grass fire. There are lots of them at this time of year."

But the alarm sounded again and again.

"It must be serious," said the mother.

"Oh, don't bother," said the neighbor. "I'm sure the fire isn't anywhere near here."

"But listen!" said the mother. "I can hear the fire engine, and it is coming this way. And look! See the people running.   9

10 They are running down this street. They are running toward my house!"

Without another word she dashed into the street and ran with the gathering crowd.

Then she saw it. Her own house was on fire! Smoke and flames were already pouring through the roof.

"My baby!" she cried frantically. "My baby!"

The crowd was thick around the house, but like one gone mad she pushed and tore her way through.

"My baby! My baby! My little Margie!"

A fireman seized her.

"You can't go!" he cried. "You will be burned to death."

"Let me go! Let me go!" she cried, breaking free and dashing into the flaming house.

She knew just where to go. Running through the smoke and flames, she seized her precious baby, then turned to make her way out. But, overcome by the smoke, she swayed and fell, and would have burned to death with her baby had not a fireman seized her and carried her out.

What a cheer went up as they appeared! But alas, though the baby was saved unharmed, the poor mother was badly hurt. Kind friends put her in an ambulance and hurried her off to the hospital. There it was found that her hands, the brave, dear hands that had lifted her baby from the blazing crib, were terribly burned. All their beauty, of which she had

been so proud, was gone. Though the doctors did their best to
save them, they were left marred and crippled.

Months later the brave mother was released from the hospital. She and her baby were together again in a new home.

Weeks became months, and months became years. The baby toddled, walked, ran. She was no longer a baby; she was a little girl. She was beginning to notice things.

One day when Marjorie was eight years old, her mother was washing dishes in the kitchen sink.

Suddenly Marjorie saw something that she had always seen but never noticed before.

"Mother," she exclaimed, "what ugly hands you have!"

"Yes, dear," said Mother quietly, though hurt almost beyond words. "They are ugly, aren't they?"

"But why do you have ugly hands when other people have pretty hands?" said Marjorie, not knowing how every word was like a dagger in Mother's heart.

Tears filled Mother's eyes.

"Oh!—what have I done wrong?" asked Marjorie.

Then Mother took Marjorie's hand and led her to the davenport. "There's something I must tell you, dear," she said.

Then she told her story, as Marjorie had never understood it before. She told of the fire, of the people who tried to hold her back, of the wild dash into the burning house, how she lifted the baby from the flaming crib, how she fell,

12   how she was rescued, and how badly she had been burned.

"My hands were beautiful till then," she said.

Marjorie clasped the crooked hands in hers, tears streaming down her cheeks. "Mother dear," she cried, "they are the most beautiful hands in all the world!"

Children, there are other hands that were wounded for you. The hands of Jesus, the children's Friend and Saviour; the hands of Him who came down from heaven to rescue His people from sin and save them in His beautiful kingdom.

You know what happened to Jesus. Evil men drove great nails through His hands and hung Him on a cross to die.

Then they buried Him in Joseph's new tomb. But they couldn't keep Him there. He rose again and ascended to heaven, where He lives today, waiting for the glad day when He shall return.

The marks of the nails are still there. When He comes back they will still be there. We shall know Him then "by the print of the nails in His hands."

Those nailmarks will be there through all eternity. As you meet Him in the New Jerusalem or in the lovely new earth, you will know that those hands, those dear, dear hands of Jesus, were marred that you might be saved. And when you say to Him, "What happened to Your hands?" He will tell you the wonderful story of salvation over and over again. Then, with little Marjorie, you will exclaim, "They are the most beautiful hands in all the world!"

Kenny's Comfort

IT WAS KENNY'S bad luck, so he thought, to be the youngest in a family of five children. He had one big sister and three big brothers, and he—well, he was just the "little 'un."

Kenny didn't like being the "little 'un," for many reasons, but chiefly because his sister and his brothers were so big and so busy that they didn't have any time to play with him. During the day they would be away at school, and when they came home in the evening they had homework to do; or they would want to go and play with friends of their own age.

So poor little Kenny felt quite lonely at times. How he did wish for a little sister—someone who would belong to him and play with him and be interested in the same things he was!

"Daddy," he would say sometimes, "can't you get me a baby sister somewhere? I do so want one."

And Daddy would say, "I wish I could, dear; but they are very hard to find. I'll keep it in mind, though."

And then Kenny would say, "But Daddy, when you go traveling sometime, couldn't you just pick one up and bring   13 her home with you? There must be lots of little girls who would like to come and live with me."

"It's not so easy as that," Daddy would reply, "but I'll keep looking and maybe, one day—well, you never know what might happen."

So Daddy went on his travels and told all his friends about his lonely little boy at home who wanted a baby sister so very much that he was even praying for one.

Oh, yes, I forgot to tell you that—Kenny was praying for a baby sister every night.

And some of Daddy's friends smiled and thought it was very funny; but it wasn't funny to Kenny. It was nothing to laugh about.

Then one day something happened.

Daddy opened a letter that said: "DEAR SIR: I have been told that you are looking for a baby girl. I happen to know of one who needs a home. She is just two-and-a-half years old and is a very sweet child. Perhaps you would like to come and see her."

Then Daddy was scared and wished he hadn't told so many people about the poor lonely little boy who wanted a baby sister. He knew that he was "on the spot," and had to decide one way or the other. He began to count up what it would cost to go and see the child, what it would cost to bring her home, what it would cost to feed her and clothe her for years and years and years.

Kenny wasn't worried, though. He thought it was just grand, and felt sure that his prayer was really going to be answered at last.

"Now don't get so excited," said Daddy; "she may not be a bit nice——"

"But the letter says she is 'very sweet,'" said Kenny.

"Well," said Daddy, "maybe we won't think she is; and anyway, perhaps something else will prevent our taking her. Just think what it will cost!"

"Oh, she won't cost much," said Kenny. "She's so little. And I'm sure she's nice. Of course she is. Anyway, Daddy, you will go to see her?"

"Well, I don't know," said Daddy. "It's a big risk. Er—er— just think——"

"Oh, don't think about it, Daddy; just go," said Kenny.

So Daddy went. There was really nothing else for him to do. And sure enough, at his journey's end, there she was, a tiny little thing with blue eyes and light curly hair—so thin and so wee and needing a home so very much.

What could he do? He looked her all over; he thought about Kenny; and then, completely forgetting all about the cost, he picked her up, and put her in his pocket—well, not quite, but almost—and brought her all the long, long way home.

When he reached home there was Kenny, eagerly waiting on the doorstep, thrilled to the innermost part of his lonely little soul.

No baby born could have had a warmer welcome. Kenny
waited on her hand and foot, washing her face, her hands,
her feet, when they got dirty—as they so often did—putting
her to bed at night, dressing her in the morning, tying on her
bib at mealtimes, and looking after her with a big brother's
devotion.

And how beautifully they played together! Kenny found
his old tricycle and fixed it up so that Little Sister could ride
on it. Of course, *he* was much too big for a tricycle now and
had a bicycle of his own. So round and round the house they
would go, shrieking with delight and having the grandest
time together.

When they got tired of riding, Kenny would put Little Sister in his wagon and take her across the lawn and round the
garden paths, running so fast that she had to hold on with all
her might to keep from falling out.

They were so happy that a stranger looking at them
might well have thought that they had known each other all
their little lives.

Six months later Daddy and Kenny were out one day
alone together.

"Now, Kenny, don't you think it's about time we sent the
little girl back?" said Daddy.

"Oh, no!" cried Kenny.

"Do you really want to keep her?"

"Of course I do, always," said Kenny.

"But why?" asked Daddy.

"'Cos she's my comfort," said Kenny.

And she really was. Never again did Kenny say he was
lonely.

◀ Painting by Russell Harlan

**Tired of riding his bicycle, Kenny would put
Little Sister in his wagon and drag her across
the lawn and around the garden paths.**

Locked in the Cupboard

WHILE WE are still thinking about Kenny and his little sister, I must tell you another story about them which could have been—but for her—quite a sad story.

You see, they were playing hide-and-seek together one day, having such a happy time. First Kenny would hide, calling out, "Ready!" when he was safely tucked away somewhere. Then Little Sister would wander all around the house and out in the garden, looking high and low for him.

To tell you the truth, she wasn't very good at finding anything or anybody, but she would hunt and hunt until at last she would come to the right place. Then there would be a big yell of excitement as the children saw each other again.

After that, Little Sister would hide. At least, she would try to hide, for it was very difficult to go anywhere that Kenny did not know about; and soon there would be another big shout as she was discovered.

Now it so happened that a new cupboard had just been built in Mother's laundry, which stood some distance away from the house, near the garage. As soon as the carpenter had finished it, Kenny said to himself, "What a place to hide

18

Fred Collins, Artist ▶

in!" He made up his mind that the very next chance he got, he would get inside that cupboard, and then Little Sister would never find him.

The chance soon came. Kenny crept silently into the laundry, opened the cupboard door, and bending down low, managed to squeeze himself between the two bottom shelves of the cupboard. The shelves, by the way, were about twenty-six inches wide and eleven inches deep, with just sixteen inches between them! There was no room to spare.

Quite sure that he was well hidden this time, Kenny called, "Read—y! Read—y!"

Suddenly a gust of wind swept through the open window of the laundry. Click!

The door of the cupboard had blown shut and the latch had snapped into place! Kenny was trapped inside, in pitch darkness, wedged between the two shelves.

Terrified, he called and called and called, but nobody heard him, for Mother was out shopping, Daddy was busy in the house, and Little Sister was looking everywhere else but in the laundry.

Meanwhile the tiny space inside the cupboard became hotter and hotter, for the only air that could come in entered by the crack at the edge of the door. Poor Kenny started to cry, as well he might. Then he prayed, oh, so hard, "Jesus, please send somebody to let me out."

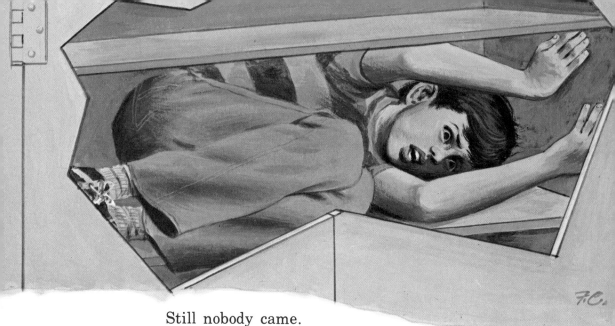

Still nobody came.

He called and called.

There was no reply.

It got hotter and hotter, and more and more uncomfortable, for he was terribly cramped. He couldn't lift his head, or stretch his arms or legs. Even his toes were bent, and he couldn't straighten them.

Ten minutes passed; twenty minutes; thirty minutes. And each minute seemed like a year.

Far away he could hear Little Sister calling, "Kenny, where are you?" But he couldn't tell her where he was, for the cupboard walls wouldn't let his voice travel so far.

Then he heard a sound that brought new hope to his poor little heart. It was the pat, pat, pat of tiny feet coming toward the laundry. Kenny had never heard such a welcome sound in all his life; it was like the footfalls of an angel!

"Here I am!" he cried, and he heard the pat, pat, pat come right inside the laundry.

"Where are you?" asked Little Sister, looking around in wonder at hearing a voice but seeing nobody.

"In the new cupboard," cried Kenny. "Come and open it—quick!"

"I can't," said Little Sister. "The handle is too high up."

"Oh, try, try," cried Kenny. "Stand on tiptoe and try."

Little Sister, frightened by the sound of Kenny's voice, tried her very best. She stood up on the very tips of her toes and reached up just as high as she could. There was a click as she pressed back the catch, then a shout of joy as Kenny tumbled out from between the two shelves.

Can you guess what happened next? Well, Kenny picked Little Sister up in his arms and kissed her over and over again. In all his life he will never forget how she came to his rescue and saved him from his terrible prison in the dark, hot cupboard.

Then they ran indoors to tell Daddy all about it; and he said that he thought it was a very foolish thing for any little boy or girl to hide in a cupboard or anything of that kind. Many children who have hidden in a closed place, especially a refrigerator, have never been found until it was too late. He said that neither of them was to hide in a cupboard again. Then he kissed them both.

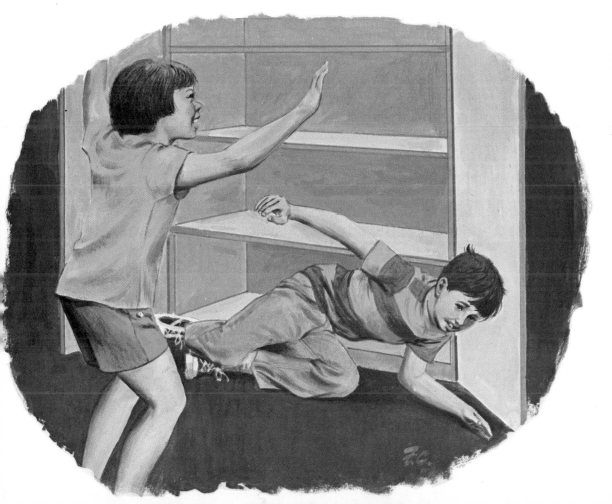

STORY **4**

Joe's Dollar

THIS IS ANOTHER little story that I'm sure you will like, for it really happened.

Joe was just eight years old. His parents were poor and were never able to give him very much pocket money. Just a nickel or a dime now and then, you know.

Then one day somebody gave him a dollar. A silver dollar! A millionaire never felt so rich.

Joe was so pleased with his dollar that he kept taking it out of his pocket to look at it. How shiny bright it was! And what a great many things it would buy!

Then some time later, as Joe put his hand into his pocket to have another look at his dollar, it was not there! He pulled the pocket inside out, but in vain. He searched all his other pockets, but the coin was in none of them. Frantically he began searching the house, the garden, everywhere he might have been. But still no dollar. To think that his one precious dollar had vanished so soon! It was terrible. He prayed, "O Lord, please help me find my lost dollar." But no dollar was to be found. He was heartbroken.

22   Evening came, and very much discouraged and out of

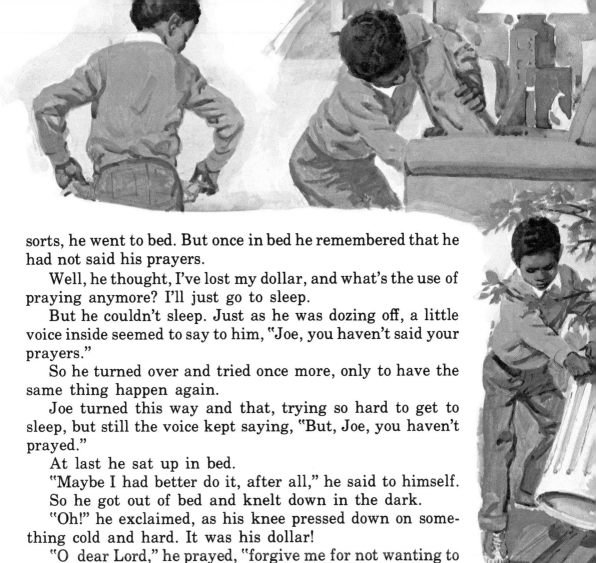

sorts, he went to bed. But once in bed he remembered that he had not said his prayers.

Well, he thought, I've lost my dollar, and what's the use of praying anymore? I'll just go to sleep.

But he couldn't sleep. Just as he was dozing off, a little voice inside seemed to say to him, "Joe, you haven't said your prayers."

So he turned over and tried once more, only to have the same thing happen again.

Joe turned this way and that, trying so hard to get to sleep, but still the voice kept saying, "But, Joe, you haven't prayed."

At last he sat up in bed.

"Maybe I had better do it, after all," he said to himself.

So he got out of bed and knelt down in the dark.

"Oh!" he exclaimed, as his knee pressed down on something cold and hard. It was his dollar!

"O dear Lord," he prayed, "forgive me for not wanting to say my prayers. I do thank You for my dollar."

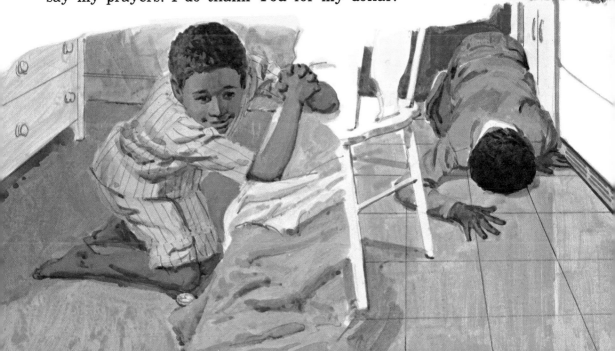

How Johnny Got Wet

MISS GIBSON WAS SITTING at her desk marking the attendance record.

"Everybody seems to be in school on time today," she said. "That is, all except Johnny. Has anybody seen Johnny?"

No one spoke.

"Does anybody know whether Johnny is ill?"

A hand went up.

"He can't be ill, Miss Gibson, for I saw him fishing in the creek yesterday evening."

"Thank you," said Miss Gibson, closing the book. "And now, I'll be back in just a moment. Please, all of you, be good and quiet until I return."

She had barely walked across the corridor, however, when the classroom door opened, and in walked Johnny. Immediately bedlam broke loose.

"Johnny!" cried one of the boys. "What have you been doing?"

"Johnny!" cried another. "What a mess you're in! Where have you been?"

They had reason to ask. For never had a boy come to   25

◀ Painting by Kreigh Collins

Johnny jumped off the bridge on his way to school and saved the life of a little girl who had fallen into the river.

school quite like this. Johnny was actually dripping wet. His hair was all mussed up as if he had been swimming. His clothes were sodden, and his shoes squished water as he walked.

"Ha! Ha! Ha!" laughed everybody. "He! He! He!" "What a sight!" "What a way to come to school!"

Suddenly the door handle rattled. Instantly there was silence. Johnny moved swiftly to his desk and sat down.

The teacher entered and looked around.

"So you are here at last, Johnny," she said. "Have you any excuse for being late?"

Then she took a closer look at him.

"What has happened to your hair?" asked Miss Gibson.

"Nothing," said Johnny, trying in vain to make it go into place.

"Stand up!"

Johnny stood up. Then she saw his wet shirt and his soggy trousers. He looked as if he wanted to crawl out of sight.

A hand was raised.

"Please, Miss Gibson, there's a puddle under Johnny's seat."

At this laughter broke out all over the classroom.

"Silence!" said Miss Gibson.

"Johnny, have you, or haven't you, an excuse? Why are you dripping wet?"

"Well—er—" began Johnny.

Just what he was going to say next nobody knows, for just at that moment the door opened again, and this time the principal, with two policemen behind him, walked into the room, and right up to the teacher's desk.

"Do you have a boy here named Johnny Gordon?" he asked. "The police——"

"The police!" whispered all the children.

"There he is," said Miss Gibson.

"The police," said the principal, "have just come here to ask about him. They say he jumped off the bridge on his way to school this morning and saved the life of a little girl who had fallen into the river and was drowning. Are you the boy?" he said, turning to Johnny.

"Yes, sir."

"I'm proud of you, son. That was a brave thing to do. God bless you. But why did you come to school like this? Why didn't you go back home and change?"

"I was afraid my dad would be angry with me for getting my clothes soaked," said Johnny.

"Well, he's not angry with you," said the principal. "I've been talking with him. He's as proud of you as I am." Then, turning to the class, he said, "We're all proud of him, aren't we, children?"

Suddenly everybody was cheering. And the very ones who had been laughing at Johnny a few minutes before cheered the loudest. How wonderful it seemed to have a real hero right in their own classroom!

"And now, Johnny, you had better run home and put on some dry clothes," said the principal, "or you'll catch a bad cold."

With teeth chattering, Johnny ran all the way home.

And soon the whole town was talking of the brave boy who saved a little girl from drowning on his way to school.

STORY **6**

The Tears
of Jesus

SOME TIME AGO I heard a great preacher say, "I want so to live as to wipe away the tears of Jesus."

It made me think. Does Jesus cry? And how can anyone wipe His tears away?

Then I thought about that little text—the shortest in the Bible—"Jesus wept." John 11:35.

From this text we know He wept once—and that was when Mary and Martha were crying over the death of their brother, Lazarus.

He wept again when He sat on the Mount of Olives, looking down upon Jerusalem. This time it was because He was thinking of all that the poor people of this city would suffer in days to come.

He never cried for Himself—only for others.

You cry when you hurt yourself, or when someone has been unkind to you, or when Mamma spanks you because you have been naughty. But Jesus didn't cry even on the cross. When the soldiers drove the nails through His hands He just prayed and prayed, "Father, forgive them; for they know not what they do."

29

Paintings by Russell Harlan © by Review and Herald ▶

Every disobedient act grieves the heart of Jesus just as every kind deed done in His name wins His smile and approval.

32   Does He cry today? I wouldn't be surprised. If He cried when He thought of what was going to happen to the people of Jerusalem in the long ago, how do you suppose He must feel as He looks down from heaven upon the whole wide world, with all its sorrow and sadness, knowing what is going to happen to it soon?

When He sees so many dear boys and girls going the wrong way, growing up to be selfish, unkind, hardhearted, cruel, I think He must be very sad indeed, especially knowing that none of them—unless converted—will ever see the beautiful kingdom He is preparing for those who love Him.

But how can anyone wipe away His tears?

By being good? That will help, of course. So will being kind, truthful, honest, unselfish, and obedient.

Yet there is something that will wipe away His tears more quickly than anything else.

Can you guess what it is?

It is being thoughtful of others. It is making others happy. Most important of all, it is leading others to love Him.

Just as it was the thought of other people's suffering that caused Him to cry when He was here on earth, so it is the thought of other people being saved from suffering—from all the sad results of sin—that brings the greatest happiness to His heart today.

Wouldn't it be lovely if every boy and girl who reads these lines would say, "I want so to live as to wipe away the tears of Jesus"?

Won't you say it—and mean it—now?

STORY **7**

How Daddy's Fence Was Saved

AS PHILIP AND GLENNYS came home from school one day they saw clouds of smoke billowing up into the air.

At first they thought their home might be on fire. But no. As they drew nearer they saw that the smoke was coming from a strip of land covered with long grass and brush.

"Let's go and watch," said Philip.

"Let's," said Glennys, and away they ran toward the fire.

As they ran they noticed that the wind was rising, whipping up the flames, causing them to leap at great speed across the land, and destroy everything in their path.

Suddenly they noticed something else—something that struck fear to their hearts.

"Look!" cried Philip. "Daddy's fence! The fire is sweeping straight toward it!"

"It's going to be all burned up!" cried Glennys. "Poor Daddy! Then he will have to build a new one. Can't we do something to save it?"

"Nobody could save it now," said Philip.

Both looked on help-lessly as the fire moved swiftly toward the fence.

"Jesus could," said Glennys.

"He *could,*" said Philip, "but would He bother about a fence?"

"We could ask Him," said Glennys.

"All right then," said Philip, "let's. But we'd better be quick or it will be all burned up." So the two children knelt down on the ground on that lonely ranch in Western Australia and prayed with all the earnestness of their hearts: "Please, Jesus, don't let the fire burn Daddy's fence. We can't stop it, but You can. Please stop it right away. Amen."

They opened their eyes. The fire was still moving toward the fence. Already the clouds of smoke were pouring over it, while the fingers of flame were reaching out and setting the posts ablaze.

Then all of a sudden the smoke rose straight into the air. Next moment it was blowing back in the opposite direction. The wind had changed!

The fire stopped moving. It went within a few feet of the fence and then died out.

As long as they live, Philip and Glennys will remember that great and wonderful day when God saved Daddy's fence —right before their eyes.

8

The Time to Obey

IT WAS HOLIDAY TIME, and the whole family had gone to the lake. Mother, Daddy, Uncle Albert, Grandma, and Barbara had taken a lovely cottage near the most beautiful sandy beach you could imagine.

The days were warm and bright, and everybody would have been perfectly happy if only Barbara had not made such a little nuisance of herself.

The big trouble was that she just would not do what she was told. She seemed to feel that she was too grown up to take notice of what anybody said, even though she was only a very little girl.

If Mother called her to come in to supper, she would dawdle and dawdle around until Mother had to fetch her; and of course nobody was happy about that, least of all Barbara.

If Mother asked her to do some small job in the kitchen, Barbara would take her own sweet time before doing it. It never seemed to occur to her that when Mother spoke, she expected to be obeyed right away.

One lovely afternoon everybody put on swim suits for a swim in the lake. Everybody, that is, except Grandma. She said she would rather sit on a folding chair on the beach.

When Mother and Daddy and Uncle Albert were all ready to go into the water, Mother said, "Let's stay in the shallow water for a while and play with Barbara; then she can stay with Grandma while we swim farther out."

"That'll be fine," said Daddy. "Come on, Barbara, let's have some fun."

But do you think Barbara would go in the water just then? No, indeed.

She wanted to play in the sand. She wanted to sit beside Grandma. She wanted to do anything and everything except what Mother and Daddy wanted her to do.

"Come on, dear," said Mother. "It's beautiful in the water. You'll love it. Come on, now."

"No," said Barbara, "I want to make some sand pies with my bucket and spade."

38   "You can do that afterward. Come and have fun in the water now while we're all here."

"No," said Barbara. "Don't want to."

"Very well," said Daddy. "Let her stay. We'll go swimming."

"All right," said Uncle Albert. "Let's go."

So Daddy, Mother, and Uncle Albert waded out through the water till it was deep enough for them to swim. Then they dived under and away they went.

No sooner were they well out into the lake than Barbara decided that she wanted to follow them.

"I'm coming, Mommy," she said, and waded in.

"Come back!" cried Grandma, but Barbara took no notice. On and on she walked, the water coming a little higher up her legs every step she took.

Suddenly Mother caught sight of her.

"Go back! Go back!" she yelled.

Still Barbara walked farther in, the water coming almost
up to her neck.

"Go back!" yelled Daddy.

"Go back!" yelled Uncle Albert.

Then, all of a sudden, Barbara disappeared. She had stepped into a hole and gone under.

Next moment Mother, Daddy, and Uncle Albert were all swimming frantically toward the spot. Grandma waded in, too, till her dress was awash.

Uncle Albert reached the spot first. Diving down, he found Barbara under the water and dragged her to the surface. Then he carried her to the beach and they all took turns rubbing her and squeezing her until she began to breathe again.

Barbara wrote and told me all about it. She said she was sick for some time before she got all better again. She told me, too, that she would never forget what happened that day at the lake, and how ever since she has told herself that the time to obey Mother is RIGHT NOW!

STORY **9**

The Man
Who Always
Said His Prayers

JOHN AND HIS MOTHER were in a city restaurant. It was packed with people, and they were waiting more or less patiently to be served. At last the waitress appeared, bringing them their dinner.

John, who was very hungry, seized his knife and fork, and prepared to eat. Then he hesitated.

Mother had bowed her head to say grace. John looked at her, then at the people all around, and blushing just a little, took his first bite.

"You didn't forget something, did you?" asked Mother, as she started to eat.

"No," said John, "but everybody was looking at me."

"But what does that matter?" asked Mother. "If it is right to thank God for our food at home, surely we should do it everywhere we go."

"But people stare," said John. "I feel uncomfortable."

"You shouldn't," said Mother. "We should never be afraid of people when we are doing right."

John went on eating in silence. The matter was apparently forgotten.

40

But when John asked for a story that night, Mother had
one ready for him. Indeed, John was surprised how quickly
Mother thought of one this time, for sometimes she took a
long time to do so.

"This is the story," said Mother, "of the man who always
said his prayers."

"What, prayed all day long?" asked John.

"Oh, no," said Mother, "but he always said his prayers, no
matter what people said of him or how they treated him. His
name was Daniel, and it was his practice to pray three times
a day, once in the morning when he got up, once at dinnertime, and once just before he went to bed."

"That's once more than we do," said John.

"Yes," said Mother, "and that is perhaps why he was such
a good man. Anyhow, that was his habit. Now, in those days
people did not live in houses like ours. There was no glass in
their windows, and unless the curtains were drawn, people
could readily see in. So it often happened that passers-by saw
Daniel praying in his room. They did not disturb him, but
they peered in, wondering, perhaps, just what he was doing.

"One day some of his enemies happened to pass the window, and seeing Daniel at prayer, thought of a new way of
causing him harm. Having much influence with the king,
they went to him with a decree they had written out and
asked him to sign it. They said, 'We want you to make a law
that if anyone asks a petition of any god or man other than
yourself during the next month, he shall be cast to the lions.'

42   Of course it was a very foolish decree, but the king, feeling flattered at the idea, signed it, and it became law.

"At once the law was published all over the kingdom, and people began to wonder how it would work out. Many knew about Daniel's habit of saying his prayers three times a day, and they said to one another, 'I wonder what he will do now?'

"Early the next morning people began to gather round Daniel's house. 'Will he pray at his window, as usual?' was the question on everybody's lips.

"More and more people came. Every eye was fixed on Daniel's window.

"At last the hour of prayer arrived. Daniel knelt in his usual place and prayed as he had always done. He made no attempt to draw the curtains and hide himself, though he could easily have done so."

"Did he know about the law?" asked John.

"Oh, yes," said Mother, "he must have known. He was the chief ruler of the land, next to the king, and his servants would surely have brought him word about what his enemies had persuaded the king to do in his absence. That is why what he did was so brave. He realized what he might have to suffer for saying his prayers, but he said them just the same.

"How the people must have stared in astonishment and disbelief as they saw him kneeling there! I'm sure some said, 'Brave man!' and others, 'How dare he disobey the king?'

"His enemies were there, too, and they at once ran off to tell the king. They were overjoyed that Daniel had so soon fallen into the trap they had laid for him.

"'Do you know,' they said to the king, 'that fellow Daniel has actually dared to defy your decree already? He is saying his prayers as usual now. You must have him arrested and cast to the lions at once.'

"Now, the king thought a great deal of Daniel. He knew that Daniel was a good man, and he valued his wise counsel in caring for his kingdom. The last thing he wanted was to

H. BAERG

see Daniel cast to the lions. He felt so sorry that his foolish
pride had led him to sign the decree. If only he had thought
about it more, he would have realized that his faithful minis-
ter would be affected by it. Now, however, he could do nothing. Try as he would, he could find no way out. Having signed
the decree, he had to abide by it. So at last, very reluctantly,
he gave orders that Daniel should be cast to the lions.

"The soldiers went round to Daniel's house and carried
him off. Great crowds of people watched him being taken
away, and followed him to the den of lions. They saw the
gates opened and the poor man thrown in. Most of them ex-

pected that he would be killed in a moment, but a great surprise awaited them.

"Even in the den of lions, with the great beasts pacing up and down around him, Daniel prayed to God. And God heard and answered him.

"All that night the king could not sleep, and very early in the morning he went alone to the den of lions and cried sorrowfully, 'O Daniel, servant of the living God, has your God, whom you serve continually, been able to deliver you from the lions?'

"Then to his great joy the king heard a familiar voice from the den, and Daniel said, 'My God sent his angel, and shut the lions' mouths, that they have not hurt me.'

"At this the king was ever so glad, and at once commanded that Daniel should be taken out of the pit and his enemies thrown in. After that he made another decree, which he sent out to every part of his kingdom, telling of the power of the great God whom Daniel served and worshiped. 'I make a decree,' he wrote, 'that in all my royal dominion men tremble and fear before the God of Daniel, for he is the living God, enduring for ever; and his kingdom shall never be destroyed, and his dominion shall be to the end. He delivers and rescues, he works signs and wonders in heaven and on earth, he who has saved Daniel from the power of the lions.'

"And so," concluded Mother, "because Daniel was faithful in saying his prayers every day, no matter who was looking at him, or what he might have to suffer for it, these beautiful words of the king about the power of Daniel's God were sent out to all the people of his kingdom. Who can tell how much good they accomplished?"

John was silent for a little while.

"I wish I had said grace at dinnertime today, Mother," he said presently. "I think Daniel would have done it."

"You'll remember it next time," said Mother.

And you may be sure that he did.

◀ Painting by Harry Baerg © by Review and Herald

God sent His angel to protect Daniel from the hungry lions, and they did not touch him.

Jimmy and the Jam Jars

JIMMY HAD A GREAT liking for jam. Indeed, he loved it. In this, of course, he was not very different from most other little boys of his age—and girls, too, for that matter. But Jimmy, well, he couldn't even look at a jam jar without feeling all stirred up inside.

Now, it so happened that one fine day Mother had spent the whole morning making strawberry jam. She had filled twenty or thirty jars, some large, some small, and by early afternoon they were all standing in neat rows in the top of her kitchen cabinet.

What a pleasing picture they made, with big strawberries clearly to be seen amid the thick red jelly.

Happy to think that her task was done, with all the dirty dishes and saucepans cleaned and put away, Mother decided to go out visiting for a little while.

"Jimmy," she said, as she came downstairs with her hat and coat on, "I'm going across to see Mrs. Brown for a few minutes. I'll be back soon. Be a good boy while I'm away."

"All right, Mother," said Jimmy. "Don't worry. I'll be real good, you'll see."

"You have plenty of things to play with, haven't you?"

"Oh, yes, Mother," said Jimmy. "I think I'll play with my trains."

"That's a good idea," said Mother. "And, by the way, I think it would be better for you not to go into the kitchen."

"All right, Mother. Why?"

"Oh, well," said Mother, thinking of her newly made jam, "just because—er—well, I think you had better not. Now, good-by, Jimmy, and be good."

"Good-by, Mother," said Jimmy, waving his hand and then running to play with his trains.

Unfortunately, Mother was gone much longer than she expected. It often happens that way, you know.

Meanwhile Jimmy got tired of playing with his trains and turned to his bricks, then to his trucks. At last he decided he didn't want to play with anything anymore, and started to walk around the house, looking for something to do.

From the kitchen there still came the sweet odor of newly

made jam, and Jimmy thought it was a very nice smell indeed. He went to the kitchen door and peeked in. Everything was very clean and tidy, and he could not see any particular reason why his mother should not want him to go in there. So in he went and wandered around.

As he walked about he kept saying to himself, "I wonder where Mom put all that jam."

Suddenly he looked upward, and, lo, there it was, all of it, on the three top shelves of the old-fashioned kitchen cabinet. The bright-red jars looked like rows of old-time soldiers such as one sees sometimes in picture books.

"What a fine lot of jam!" exclaimed Jimmy.

He looked and looked and looked.

"I wonder," he said to himself after a while, "if Mother would mind if I were to open the cupboard door and look at it a little closer?"

As Mother wasn't there to answer his question, he decided to answer it himself, and proceeded to carry a stool over to the base of the cabinet.

Now, Mother had an old-fashioned kitchen cabinet, made in two parts. There was a top half and a bottom half, and the one sat lightly on the other.

Unfortunately, Jimmy didn't know that.

Standing on the stool, he was just able to reach the knob on the glass door, which he gently pulled. The two doors swung open, revealing to Jimmy a wonderful array of jam jars.

"I wonder," he said to himself, "if Mother would mind if I were to taste just a little bit—just a very little bit. There is so much that I don't think Mother would even notice it, and I'm sure she wouldn't mind."

So Jimmy reached up and began trying to open one of the jam jars.

Alas! Just at that moment the stool slipped away from under his feet. To save himself, Jimmy clutched desperately

at one of the shelves of the cabinet and——

Crash!

In an instant Jimmy, cabinet, and jam jars had become one dreadful, sticky mess on the kitchen floor.

At that very moment Mother was nearing the house, on her way home from Mrs. Brown's. Hearing the crash, she dashed indoors, only to find Jimmy lying on the floor buried beneath the remains of her strawberry jam.

"Oh, my poor Jimmy!" she said, rushing toward him. "He's dead. I'm sure he's dead. My poor dear little Jimmy!"

But Jimmy wasn't dead. At least, something was moving under the cabinet, and as Mother lifted it up, Jimmy rose to his feet. What a sight he was! He looked for all the world like a piece of bread and butter spread with jam. He was covered

4-4

50   with jam from head to foot. There was jam in his hair and jam on his shirt, jam on his trousers and jam on his shoes.

Mother took Jimmy over to the sink and began to wash the jam out of his eyes and ears. Then she found that he wasn't really hurt at all—not a single cut anywhere, despite all that broken glass!

Then a new note came into Mother's voice. She was cross and no doubt about it.

"You naughty little boy!" she cried. "How dare you disobey me like that! Look at all my jam! Look at my cabinet all broken to pieces! You bad boy, you!"

At this point Mother began walking towards the stairs, with Jimmy's hand held tightly in hers.

Just what happened upstairs I will leave you to imagine, but Jimmy told me—yes, he told me himself—that in all the years that have gone by since then he has never forgotten what happened that afternoon, and—what matters most of all—he has never, never disobeyed his mother from that day to this.

11

All Because They Quarreled

BANG! WALLOP! BANG! Tom and Eric were punching each other as hard as they could.

"Take that!" shouted Eric angrily, landing another blow on Tom's right cheek.

"And you take that!" cried Tom, striking Eric's nose with his clenched fist.

"Stop it, boys!" a man's voice broke in. "No more of this! Break it up now!"

Tom and Eric looked up to see old Barney, the friendly boatman with the short arm, looking down at them. Of course, they couldn't go on fighting with him standing by, so they put their hands in their pockets and stood glaring at each other.

"Come and sit on my boat a minute," said the old man, "and I'll tell you a story."

Meekly the boys did as old Barney suggested, Tom walking on one side of him and Eric on the other. Soon all three were sitting on the overturned boat.

"When I was a boy," old Barney began, "my brother and I used to play with hoops."

51

52   "Hoops?" asked Eric. "What's a hoop?"

"It was a narrow piece of iron made into a circle about four feet across. Girls and small boys had wooden hoops and bowled them along with sticks. Bigger boys used an iron hook to drive their iron hoops. It was fixed in a small wooden handle and acted as a brake when running downhill.

"Well, one day my older brother and I were out playing with our hoops. I was using a stick to bowl mine along while he had an iron hook, as he was a couple of years older.

"By and by I asked him to let me try his hook, but he wouldn't lend it to me.

"He said I was only a little kid and I just wouldn't know what to do with it.

"I said I was just as well able to use it as he was, and if he would let me have it for a little while I would soon show him.

"He said he wouldn't think of lending it to such a little shrimp, so I punched him in the stomach. Then he hit me on the ear, and the fight was on.

"As we fought, my brother dropped his iron hook and I made a grab for it. To keep me from getting it, he gave me a push, and I fell over, hitting my arm on the granite curb.

"Suddenly I yelled with pain and lay on the ground, unable to get up. Somebody came and picked me up, but I yelled again, since my arm hurt so badly.

"When I tried to raise my arm I found I couldn't, and I be- came very frightened. So did my brother, who now tried to console me.

53

"When I tried to raise my arm I found I couldn't, and I be-   53
came very frightened. So did my brother, who now tried to
console me.

"Then a man came along who knew something about first
aid. He took one look at my arm and said it was broken and
that I must be taken to a doctor.

"Then I was carried home. Mother was terribly upset. She
put on her hat and coat, and off we all went to the doctor.

"He cut my sleeve away and looked at my arm. He said I
had a compound fracture and dislocation. So he set my arm
and put it in splints. But it didn't set right. I had to have two
operations, but it never got straight again. Today it is five
inches shorter than my other arm."

"I always wondered why you had one short arm," said

54 Tom, with sympathy in his voice. "I'm glad you told us what happened."

"Yes," said old Barney, "and it was all because we quarreled all those long, long years ago."

"That's why you stopped us fighting just now, wasn't it?" said Eric.

"That's just exactly why," said old Barney. "When I see boys fighting I'm always scared somebody's going to get hurt and suffer as I have done. It isn't worth it, boys. I know. Mark my words, it isn't worth it."

Old Barney was right. It isn't worth it.

Quarreling doesn't do anybody any good.

12

Motorboat Miracle

MOTORBOATS HAVE ALWAYS thrilled me. I love to read about them and dream about them, don't you?

But here is a motorboat story that is quite different. I am sure you never read anything like it before. Yet it is absolutely true.

It happened during the war in the South Pacific. The motorboat, a fine mission launch, was taken over by the military soon after war was declared. Naturally the missionary in charge was sorry to give it up, but there was nothing else to do, with the enemy drawing nearer every week. The native Christians were sorry, too, for they knew this boat well, and to them it was a messenger of light, going from island to island to visit the people with the good tidings of God's redeeming love.

Some time later, when the Allied forces were compelled to leave the islands, the military decided to destroy the mission launch in order to prevent its falling into the enemy's hands. So they sent someone to pour gasoline over the little vessel and set a match to it. There was a sudden explosion and a spurt of flame. But a sharp gust of wind blew out the flames,

55

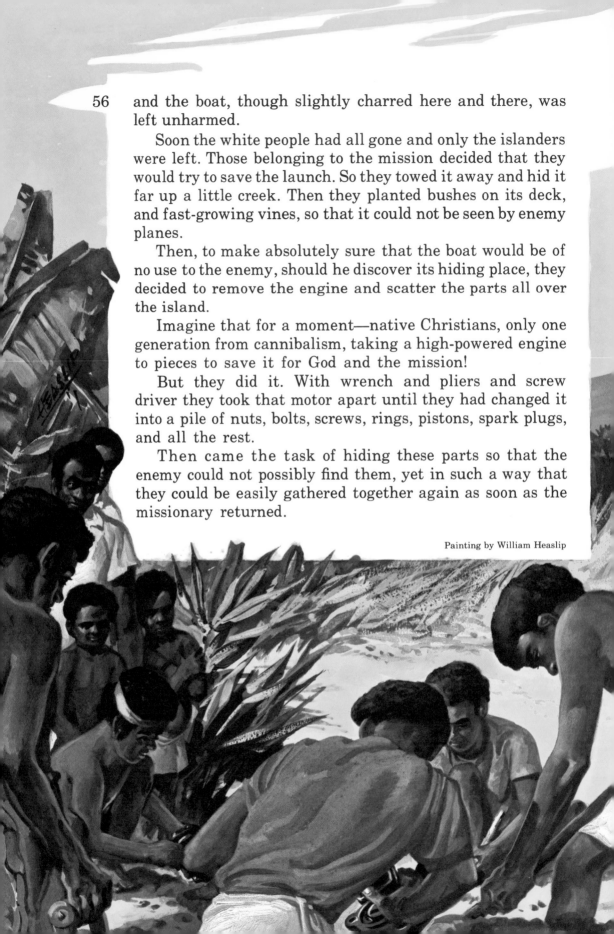

56 and the boat, though slightly charred here and there, was left unharmed.

Soon the white people had all gone and only the islanders were left. Those belonging to the mission decided that they would try to save the launch. So they towed it away and hid it far up a little creek. Then they planted bushes on its deck, and fast-growing vines, so that it could not be seen by enemy planes.

Then, to make absolutely sure that the boat would be of no use to the enemy, should he discover its hiding place, they decided to remove the engine and scatter the parts all over the island.

Imagine that for a moment—native Christians, only one generation from cannibalism, taking a high-powered engine to pieces to save it for God and the mission!

But they did it. With wrench and pliers and screw driver they took that motor apart until they had changed it into a pile of nuts, bolts, screws, rings, pistons, spark plugs, and all the rest.

Then came the task of hiding these parts so that the enemy could not possibly find them, yet in such a way that they could be easily gathered together again as soon as the missionary returned.

Painting by William Heaslip

Some of the larger parts, like the cylinder block and the crankcase, they buried in the sand, but the crankshaft was tied to the branch of a tall tree. As for the nuts, bolts, washers, and little things like that, they were carefully tied together, a few at a time, and hung round the necks of the Christian believers. They guessed that the Japanese would presume that they were just wearing charms like the heathen natives, and they guessed right. And they wore those "charms" round their necks until the war ended. No enemy spy once suspected what they really were.

At last the tide of war turned. The Japanese fled, and the Allies came back. Shortly after that the missionary himself returned.

When the local believers saw him, they greeted him with great joy. Then they asked him if he would like to see the mission launch.

"The mission launch?" he said. "But that

was burned and sunk long ago. Our mission board received official word about it from the government."

"But it did not burn," they told him.

So they took the missionary up the little creek, and there she was, still riding the water, all covered over with greenery.

Then they cleaned off the bushes, the vines, the moss, and the rest of the camouflage, and the marveling missionary went aboard.

What a dreadful wreck it seemed to be! Surely it would never go to sea again.

Then he looked in the engine room, and gasped in dismay.

"Look! The engine's gone!" he cried. "We can't use her now. Why, they've taken every bolt and nut."

"Yes, sir," said the leader. "We took it apart to save it from the enemy."

"You did!" exclaimed the missionary. "And where are the parts? Can you find them?"

"Just wait and see."

Then the drums sounded and the church bells

Painting by William Heaslip

rang, and the message echoed up the valleys and over the mountains: "The missionary is back. Bring in the parts for the mission launch!"

In response there began the most amazing procession that anyone has ever seen. Two men staggered up with the cylinder block. Another two brought the crankshaft. Then from far and near came men and women with their strings of "beads" or "charms," and placed them before the missionary, symbol of a loyalty we can hardly imagine.

60   When it was over, there was a pile of parts big enough to frighten the most skilled engineer at General Motors, it would seem to me.

Fortunately, the missionary was something of a mechanic and, believe it or not, two months later he had that engine going again, purring like a Persian cat after a good, satisfying meal.

Not a single part was missing! Indeed, there were a few parts left over that the missionary didn't know what to do with. All had been kept in safety, as something sacred and precious, by these dark-skinned, South Pacific children of God.

No wonder there was great rejoicing by all the people in the whole area as the launch sailed out to sea once more. It had been saved by a miracle—a miracle of faithfulness and love.

It Wasn't
"Quite Safe"

"OH, COME ON, Mother!" said Dickie. "If you won't let me have a whole box of matches, just let me have one or two."

"No," said Mother firmly. "Matches were not made to be played with. They are much too dangerous."

"It's quite safe," said Dickie, in a scornful tone of voice. "Aw, Mother, I only want to light a little bonfire out in the garden. It won't do any harm. How can it? There's nothing in the way. Nothing to burn. Come on; let a fellow have a match."

"No," said Mother, a little more firmly than before. "You are having no matches today, Dickie. Understand that. Don't you know that we've had no rain here for weeks? Everything is as dry as tinder. Just one spark will set the whole place afire."

"No, it wouldn't," persisted Dickie. "Not where I want to light my bonfire."

"I'm sorry," said Mother. "I can't help it. There is going to be no bonfire lighted around here until after the next spell of wet weather. It isn't safe, Dickie. Be sensible."

61

"Ah-haw," snorted Dickie, bolting out of the kitchen and mumbling under his breath about its being "safe anyway."

Outside he wandered around the garden, looking for something else to do. Every now and then he would go and look at the pile of dry sticks and old wood he had gathered for his precious bonfire. Every time he saw it he felt angry that he wasn't allowed to light it.

By and by Mother came to the back door and called to him.

"I'm going to town for a little while, Dickie," she said. "Look after Sister for me till I get back. That's a good boy. I won't be very long."

After Mother had gone, Mary came out to play with Dickie, whom she adored. She soon noticed that he wasn't feeling very happy.

"What's the matter, Dickie?" she lovingly inquired. "You look so sad."

"Aw, nothing," he said. "Only I wanted to light my bonfire this afternoon, but I don't have any matches."

"I can get you some," she offered. "I know where Mother keeps them."

"But Mother said I wasn't to——" began Dickie.

"But she never said anything to me about it," said Mary. "She wouldn't mind if I got them, I know."

Dickie, of course, should have told Mary the whole story, but he didn't. He let her get the matches. That was his first mistake. The second was when he lighted one of the matches and put it to his pile of wood.

"It's safe, anyway," he said to himself, trying to quiet his conscience. "We'll just have fun for a little while, and then the fire will be out. It will be all over long before Mother comes back."

It was, but not as he expected.

In normal times it would have been quite safe to light a bonfire where Dickie had made this one; but Mother was right; after so long a dry spell a fire anywhere was dangerous.

As the match touched the twigs, sticks, and old wood that Dickie had gathered, they roared into a blaze, just as though someone had covered them with gasoline. Dickie and Mary moved away from the heat and looked on with wonder and delight at the leaping, crackling flames.

Dickie was just saying to himself again, "Of course, it's safe," when he noticed that a piece of half-burned paper, which had been flung into the air by the fierceness of the fire, was dropping some distance away in a patch of long, dry grass. He ran over to stamp it out but was too late. In an instant the grass was alight, and the flames seemed to leap yards every second, spreading in all directions.

"What shall we do?" cried Mary, as she tried to put out the blaze with her little feet.

64   "Don't worry," said Dickie, trying to look calm. "It will burn itself out. It's quite safe out here. It won't hurt anything."

But even as he spoke he was feeling very sick inside; for he knew that, while he might have covered up the ashes of the bonfire, he could never hide this great patch of blackness from his mother.

But still worse was to happen. A gentle breeze blew across the garden. The flames leaped to meet it, then turned in a new direction.

"Oh, look!" cried Mary. "The fire is going toward the chicken shed! Mother's hens are in there, and all the baby chicks! Hurry, Dickie, quick, quick! Get them out before they're all burned up."

Dickie ran, but again he was too late. Already the flames had reached the door of the chicken shed and were leaping up so high, so hungrily, that he didn't dare go any nearer to them.

"Mother's baby chicks!" screamed Mary in terror. "They'll all be burned!"

Dickie was frightened now. From inside the doomed chicken house came the most dreadful noises as the poor birds squawked their fear and flew madly against the door and windows. The poor things were trapped.

Mary and Dickie simply stood looking at the fire, crying. There was nothing else they could do. The chicken house, bone dry and with a tarred roof, flared like a torch for three or four minutes. Then it collapsed in a pile of burning embers. Mother's chickens were all dead.

Mary, weeping bitterly, went into the house. Dickie, pale as a ghost and sick at heart, found a dark hole in the basement and hid there.

What would Mother say? he thought, as he waited there all alone. What would Father do? How he wished he had not been so disobedient.

Tears were running down his cheeks now. He had never meant to do this. He wouldn't have killed Mother's chickens for anything. Mother had been right after all. It hadn't been safe to light that fire. Oh, dear! What on earth could he do?

Still crying, he fell asleep.

When he awoke he looked up to see both Mother and Father looking down at him. They had been searching for him ever since they came back from town and found all the damage he had done. They both looked very sad. But somehow they seemed to know from the look on Dickie's face that he had learned his lesson.

He had. He didn't need to be punished anymore. He told them both he would never disobey them again or question their good judgment. And he kept his word.

14

Amanda's Pet

A LITTLE GIRL sent me this story from Zambia in the heart of Africa. In her letter she said that she reads *Bedtime Stories* and she wanted to tell me about something that happened to her pet dog, Rover.

Amanda, it seems, has several dogs, but Rover is her special favorite. Every morning she runs out of the house to say good morning to him and give him his breakfast.

One day, as she was carrying Rover's food to his kennel, she noticed that he wasn't there.

Funny! she thought. Wherever can he be?

She called and called, but no Rover appeared.

"Oh, well," she said to herself, "all dogs run away sometimes, and he'll be back in a hurry when he's good and hungry."

So she gave the food to her other dogs and went off to school. But when she got back home that evening, and there was no Rover to greet her, she began to get worried. Something must have happened to him. Could he have been bitten by a snake or eaten by a crocodile?

Darkness fell, and still there was no Rover.   67

That night, before she went to sleep, Amanda prayed for her pet, that he might come home to her safely in the morning.

Morning dawned, and there was Rover, outside the back door, but oh, his poor leg! It was a terrible sight. What had happened to it Amanda never did find out, and Rover, of course, couldn't tell her.

Tenderly she bathed the wound, and wrapped the poor leg with a soft white bandage as gently as she could.

Rover whimpered a little while she worked, but he never tried to bite her. He seemed to understand that she was do-

ing her very best not to hurt him but to help his leg to get better.

Some weeks later, when Rover's leg was all healed, Amanda went romping with him along the riverbank not far from her home.

Seeing a pretty water lily near the bank, she reached over to pick it, and fell in.

As she came to the surface she screamed for help, for she couldn't swim and she couldn't touch the bottom with her feet. But nobody heard her cries. Nobody, that is, except Rover. In a flash he leaped from the bank into the deep water. Getting his teeth into Amanda's clothes, he struggled and struggled until finally he brought her near enough to the bank so that she could climb out to safety.

"So you see, Uncle Arthur," she said at the end of her letter, "it really does pay to be kind to animals."

I should say it does!

15

Brenda's Skates

IF THERE WAS one thing more than another that Brenda wanted for her birthday, it was a pair of roller skates. How she coaxed and coaxed for them! How she promised to be as good as gold for the next ten years if only Mother or Father would give her a pair!

In vain her mother explained that Brenda might not learn to use them as easily as other children, that she might fall many times and perhaps hurt herself before she could skate properly. Brenda wanted skates and that was that.

She thought about skates all day and dreamed about skates all night. She pictured herself skating to school and home again, skating to the stores for Mother, and skating all over the yard, of course. Was her birthday never going to come?

It came at last, and with it the precious parcel for which she had longed. Somehow, even before she opened it, she guessed there were skates inside. And there were. Beautiful new shiny skates. Just her size, too. What bliss! Brenda felt she had never been so happy in all her life.

And now to practice with them. Scarcely was breakfast

over before she was out on the smooth concrete in front of the garage, strapping on the skates. At last, she thought, I am going to skate!

Eagerly she stood up. But only for a moment. Suddenly, to her great surprise, away went both her feet from under her. Down she went.

Bang!

"Mother!" she cried. "That hurt."

But Mother was indoors and did not notice. So Brenda stood up again. But hardly had she put one foot forward, when the other, for some reason, started running backward, and down she went again, this time on her face.

Bang!

This really hurt, and Brenda felt very much like crying. Slowly she got up once more and started to walk. But before she knew what was happening, bang! She was sitting on the concrete again.

Somehow she just couldn't do it. Up she got and down she went. It was a case of bump, bump, bump, and bang, bang, bang, until certain parts of her were quite sore. And she felt very sad. All her hopes of skating to school and to town like the other girls faded away.

As she sat on the concrete again, tears filled her eyes. She began to wish she had never asked for skates for her birthday. Why hadn't she asked for a new doll? or a new baby car-

72   riage? She wouldn't have got hurt then.

"Horrid old skates!" she cried, unstrapping them from her feet and throwing them inside the back door with a loud clatter.

"What's the matter?" called Mother. "Tired of skating already?"

"No," said Brenda crossly. "But I can't skate. I've fallen down so often I'm sore all over."

"Don't give up yet," said Mother. "You haven't started to learn. You must keep on trying till you succeed."

"Trying!" cried Brenda. "I've tried all I'm going to. I tell you, Mother, I'm sore. Sore! And I wish I had never asked for skates."

"Oh, tut, tut!" said Mother. "You are giving up altogether too easily."

"So would you," said Brenda, "if you had fallen on the same place as many times as I have this morning. Skating is not for me."

"But, Brenda," said Mother, "you are not going to let the other girls beat you, are you?"

"I don't care," said Brenda. "I can't skate. I just can't. So there!"

"You mustn't say 'can't,'" said Mother. "You can. But while skating comes easily to some, it is very hard for others.

Why, I don't know. Once I saw two children get skates for the first time. One put them on and sailed away just as if she had skated all her life. The other fell all over the place. But she tried and tried and tried again, until now she can skate as well as anybody else."

"Do you really think I could do it, too, if I tried?" asked Brenda.

"Of course," said Mother. "And I'll come along and help you."

"Now?"

"Yes, now," said Mother.

So on went the skates once more, and down went Brenda on the same sore spot. But she got up again and, leaning on Mother, went carefully forward.

Slowly, gradually, she got the idea of how to do it, how to balance herself, how to swing her weight gently, easily, this way and that.

Now and then, when all seemed to go wrong and she was sprawled all over the concrete, she wanted to give up and throw her skates away, but Mother would insist on her keeping going.

"You must never even think you can't do it," she said. "Just keep on trying, trying, trying, no matter how many times you fall. It's just like learning to do any difficult task in life. Never give up. Keep trying till you win."

So Brenda tried and tried again. Several days later she was skating round the concrete all by herself. Soon she was out on the sidewalk with the other girls, skating to school. By trying and trying and "sticking it out" she made her dream come true.

"Behold, Your King Is Coming!"

"QUICK, CHILDREN, QUICK!" cried a voice. "He is coming along the road now." In an instant the boys and girls left the game they were playing and rushed off helter-skelter to see the sight.

From all directions, down from the hillsides and out from Jerusalem, the people were swarming in hundreds.

Like wildfire the news had spread that Jesus, the Great Teacher of Galilee, was that day to ride in triumph into Jerusalem to become King of the Jews.

How happy all the people were! At last they were to obtain their freedom from their Roman rulers. The Messiah had come to reign gloriously in Jerusalem, feeding the hungry and healing the sick.

And the children! They could scarcely contain themselves. To them Jesus was the great hero of the hour. He had always been so kind to them, so different from the other grownups, that they loved Him dearly. And to think that now He was to become their King! They were wild with delight.

"Here He comes! Here He comes!"

74   The cry was taken up by the crowds that lined the road-

side and echoed from the lips of thousands who gazed from the cottage doorways or looked down from the city walls.

Yes, there He was, riding slowly along upon a donkey, not dressed in kingly robes, but with more than kingly bearing.

As He drew nearer and nearer to the city, the excitement became still more intense. People took off their outer garments and laid them down upon the roadway in token of their loyalty and love. Others broke branches off the trees and scattered them across His path, everyone trying to do Him honor.

Then someone cried out, "Hosanna to the Son of David! Blessed is he who comes in the name of the Lord! Hosanna in the highest!"

In a moment a thousand voices repeated the welcoming words, "Hosanna! Hosanna! Hosanna in the highest!" To those on the walls of the city the voices rising from the valley sounded like the roar of the ocean waves.

Soon the long procession reached the city walls. The gates were flung wide open, and in rode Jesus on a donkey, with the boys and girls dancing around Him in glee, and the multitude following, welcoming Him as the new ruler of Israel.

Now the whole city was stirred, and everybody—men, women, and children—came to see what was going on. I don't suppose anybody remained indoors that day.

Jesus went straight to the Temple, where, finding it full of cattle dealers, salesmen, and money-changers, He drove them all out, saying to them in a commanding voice, which none dared disobey, "My house shall be called a house of prayer, but you make it a den of robbers."

In the midst of all this tumult, some blind men and some that were lame were led to Jesus. In a moment they were healed.

Thrilled by the overthrow of the cheating money-changers and the healing of the blind and the lame, the children burst out in song again: "Hosanna to the Son of David! Hosanna! Hosanna!"

At this the Pharisees came to Jesus and told Him to tell the children to stop, but He would not do it. "If they were to

stop," He said to them, "the very stones would cry out."

Then a strange thing happened. In the midst of all the excitement, when He could easily have become king if He had but said the word, Jesus quietly withdrew and went away by Himself to a little cottage in Bethany. Very few, if any, of the people saw Him go; and when they discovered that He had gone they wondered what had happened.

Many of these people never saw Jesus again until He was being led away to be crucified, and they were very much perplexed. Why did this Man, who seemed to have so much power at His command, so easily yield Himself up to His enemies? They could not understand it. Of them all, the children, I think, must have been the most keenly disappointed. They had hoped for so much from Jesus, and now He was being nailed to a cross! It was heartbreaking.

But a few days later the news spread that Jesus had risen from the dead. Jerusalem was filled with rumors. Was it really true?

Yes, it was true. Hundreds of people saw Him again—men, women, and children. Then they began to understand why He had refused to be an earthly monarch. He was a far greater King than that.

One day He went to Bethany, and in full view of His disciples, rose up into the air and went away into heaven, promising them that He certainly would come back someday and take them to be with Him.

Ever since that day people have been looking for Jesus to come back from the skies. It is now more than nineteen hundred years since He went away, but he is not going to stay away much longer.

Nearly all the events have occurred which Jesus said would take place as signs of His return; so we shall not have long to wait now. Today all over the world thousands upon thousands of men and women, boys and girls, are getting ready to meet Him. They are saying to those who do not know

◄ Painting by B. Plockhorst

The gates of the city were thrown open, and as Jesus rode in, a thousand voices shouted the welcoming words "Hosanna in the highest!"

about it, "Behold, your King is coming to you!"

And when He does come, won't we all be glad to see Him! I think the children will be the happiest of all, don't you?

Maybe He will come in the middle of some dark and stormy night. From lip to lip the cry will pass, "Jesus is coming!"

We shall jump out of our beds and run to the window, and there in the sky we shall see Him in all His glory. The darkness will be gone, and the night turned into day by the dazzling light that surrounds Him.

In that moment those who have not believed in Him will be greatly frightened, but the children who have loved Him will say, "This is the Lord; we have waited for him; let us be glad" (Isaiah 25:9).

Why Rolly
Wouldn't Eat

ROLLY HAD BEEN invited to Teddy Egan's home for dinner, and was he glad to go! It was the biggest thing that had happened in his life so far.

Rolly's mother was as excited about it as Rolly himself. She kept telling him what to do and what not to do, so that Teddy's father and mother would see what a fine Christian boy he was.

For several days it was "Rolly, mind you do this" and "Rolly, be sure not to do that," until Rolly began to get quite muddled as to just what he should and shouldn't do.

One thing that Mother made very plain was that he was not to speak unless someone spoke to him; another was that he should always say "Please" and "Thank you" at the right time. Then, of course, he must not talk with his mouth full. But the most important thing, Mother said, was that he was not to start eating until grace had been said and the others had begun to eat.

At last the great day came. Rolly, dressed in his very best suit, complete with polished shoes and a haircut, arrived at Teddy Egan's home. Teddy's mother met him at the door and   79

gave him a very friendly welcome.

Soon they went into the dining room. What a sight met Rolly's excited gaze! He had never seen such a spread in all his life. The table was loaded with delicious food, while at each place were gilt-edged plates and bright silver knives and forks. Rolly began to wonder whether he had been invited to a king's palace, it was all so very wonderful. He felt sure that he was going to have the grandest meal he had ever eaten, and he made up his mind that he would have to be on his very best behavior. Then Mr. Egan came in and they all took their places around the table.

Now it so happened that there was one important difference between Rolly's home and Teddy's. Rolly's was a Christian home, where they had family prayers, and where every meal began with the saying of grace. But in Teddy's it was quite different. Nobody ever prayed there, and certainly nobody ever said grace at meals. And that's where the trouble came.

The food was quickly passed, and Rolly smiled as he looked at the big helpings that were heaped on his plate. He thought about that Bible story of Benjamin who was given a double portion by his big brother. Rolly had just that.

He was about to start eating when he stopped and laid down his knife and fork. He had suddenly remembered something Mother had told him. Then he looked around the table. Yes, the others had all begun to eat, but they hadn't said grace! Oh dear! he thought, what shall I do?

Not knowing what to do, he just waited.

Soon Mrs. Egan noticed.

"What's the matter?" she said kindly. "Is there something wrong, Rolly? Perhaps we have given you something that you don't like."

"No, thank you," said Rolly, blushing.

"Come along then, set to," said Mr. Egan. "We've all started."

"Yes, sir, please, sir," said Rolly, turning a deeper red, but still not picking up his knife and fork.

"Aren't you feeling quite well?" asked Mrs. Egan in a worried tone of voice.

"Oh, yes, please, thank you," said Rolly. "I'm quite all right, thank you."

Mr. Egan put down his knife and fork.

"Well, what *is* the matter, son?" he said.

By this time everybody had stopped eating and was looking over at Rolly, who was beginning to wish he had never, never, never come to dinner. Oh, what should he say?

"Come, come," said Mr. Egan, "is it the potatoes or the cabbage or the gravy, or what? We will get something else if you don't like this food."

"Oh, please, it's all lovely," said poor Rolly. "It's all perfectly lovely. Only——"

"Only what?" asked Mr. Egan.

"Only it hasn't been blessed," said Rolly, at last plucking up courage to say what was on his heart. "Jesus hasn't blessed it." For half a minute there was a silence that could be felt. Mr. Egan looked at Mrs. Egan, and now it was their turn to blush.

Mr. Egan broke the silence.

"Rolly's right," he said. "Good for you, son. Thanks for reminding us. Let's all bow our heads and I'll say grace."

They bowed their heads.

"Dear God," said Mr. Egan, "we thank Thee for this food. Make us truly grateful for it. Bless it to our use. Remember all who are in need. For Jesus' sake. Amen."

Another silence followed. This time it was broken by the rattle of a knife and fork on Rolly's plate. Now that the right thing had been done, he was making up for lost time.

◄ Painting by Manning de V. Lee © by Review and Herald

Wherever we are, at home or in a restaurant, God is pleased to hear His children thank Him each mealtime for His mercies.

18

Watch Me!

JERRY WAS JUST ten years old and a big lad for his age. What muscles! What a chest! Strong as a horse, he could knock a ball farther than anyone else on his team. And he could work hard, too, when he wanted to, which wasn't very often.

The pity was that Jerry knew he was strong, and thought everybody else ought to know about it. He was forever calling attention to what he could do. He wanted people to look at him and praise him for everything he did.

"Watch me hit this ball!" he would say, or, "Watch me row this boat!" or "Watch me ride my bike!" Even when he was going to sing he would say, "Watch me hit that high note!"

It really became quite tiresome, for people don't like to watch boys who want to be watched. In fact, nobody likes the boy, or the girl, who is forever bragging about what he or she can do.

Sooner or later, of course, something always happens to those who boast about themselves. Just as the Bible says, "Pride goeth before destruction, and an haughty spirit before a fall." Proverbs 16:18.

And so it turned out with Jerry.

He was at the seaside for a vacation. On bright, calm days he was allowed to take a rowboat out on the sea all by himself, and how he did enjoy it! He could row, too. There was no doubt about that. He could make the oars go so fast that it was a job for anybody to keep up with him.

But he spoiled it all by calling out, over and over again, "Watch me!" "Watch me!" "Watch me!"

Then it happened. It was so funny you would have laughed if you could have seen it.

There was another boy in a boat following Jerry, who was fast overtaking him. Jerry saw him and tried to put on a burst of speed to keep in the lead, for he couldn't bear to have anyone get ahead of him.

"Watch me beat him!" he cried. "Watch me!"

Suddenly Jerry's right oar slipped out of the oarlock. Instantly he tipped over backward, landing on the bottom of the boat with his feet stuck up in the air where his head should have been. Meanwhile he let go of the oar, which fell into the water and was washed away.

A moment or two later Jerry picked himself up and began to look around. Then he found that he was away out on the sea with only one oar. What to do? He was a bright lad, and determined not to be beaten. So he moved one of the oarlocks to the back of the boat, rested his one oar in it and, standing up, began using it as a propeller. Sculling, it is called.

The boat started moving forward, and in a few minutes he was shouting to the people on shore again, "Watch me, everybody watch me!"

But his luck was out for that day. Just as he gave the oar a mighty heave to make the boat go faster, the oar jumped out of the oarlock once more and Jerry, losing his balance, fell headlong over the side into the sea.

All were watching him now, of course, just when he didn't want them to. Soon boats were pulling toward him from all directions. A man fished him out of the water and brought him to land. Another rescued his boat, while somebody else set out to get his two oars for him.

It was a sorry picture he made as he walked up the beach, water dripping from his hair, his shirt, his trousers, and oozing out of his shoes.

"Watch me!" cried a voice in the crowd.

Jerry turned round, his eyes ablaze. But what could he say? What could he do? Everybody was laughing, so he laughed too.

He got the point all right, and never again did he say, "Watch me!"

The Boy Who Found Black Gold

"WOULDN'T IT BE NICE if we never had to work anymore?" said Douglas, as he and his father were out for a drive during their vacation.

Father smiled, taking his eye off the roadway for a moment to look down at his nine-year-old son.

"It might be nice," he said, "but I doubt if it would be good for us. Idle hands get into mischief, you know. What is more, suppose everybody got the same idea!"

"You mean, suppose everybody stopped working at once?"

"Yes."

"That would be wonderful," said Douglas. "The whole world would have one grand vacation."

"Would it?" said Father. "Just a minute. That would mean all the farmers would stop working. And the railroad men. And the car manufacturers. And the oil producers, and everybody else. So there wouldn't be any food to buy. All the shops would be closed. Nobody could travel. You couldn't buy a car and, if you had one, you couldn't get any gasoline for it. No, it wouldn't do at all. If the world is to live, it must work. Everybody must work and pull his full share of the load."

88

"Talking of gasoline," said Douglas, "your tank is nearly
empty."

"So it is!" exclaimed Father. "We must stop at the very
next station."

They pulled up at the red pumps of a wayside service station and waited while the man put in the gasoline.

"Do you know," said Father, as they started off again,
"those red pumps are a monument to hard work. I never see
them without thinking of the man who made them possible.
My! How he worked!"

"Who was it?" asked Douglas.

"I'll tell you," said Father. "It is really the story of a boy—
a boy who found black gold."

"Go on," said Douglas, scenting a good story.

"I don't know how old he was at the time," Father went
on, "but he was not much more than a lad when he heard of
the discovery of black gold in Pennsylvania. Oil is called
black gold, you know, because it is almost as precious as gold.

"That was in 1859, when the first oil well was drilled in
America, and oil came oozing up out of the ground from a
depth of sixty-nine feet. Well, this lad, whose name was
Schofield, spent eight years looking here and there in Pennsylvania for a place that might yield oil for him. He pros-
pected for oil just as others were prospecting for gold. Then
someone told him that, away out in the West, in a place

called California, there was land that looked as if it might yield oil.

"So young Schofield traveled West, and in 1875 he began to look around southern California for the telltale signs of oil.

"After a while he got an idea that oil could be found in Pico Canyon, about seven miles from Newhall, and he made up his mind to drill there if possible. But he couldn't do it alone or without money. So he persuaded some friends to lend him some money and got another friend, Alex, a big strong fellow, to go along with him.

"The two set out for the canyon. How they worked! They didn't have any modern drilling machinery. Everything was done by hand. They drove the bit down into the ground by their own weight and energy. Then they used the spring of a bent sapling to drag it out again.

"Day after day they toiled in the burning heat, pushing the bit into the hole, then waiting for it to be yanked out again by the pull of the bent tree. At the end of thirty days they had gone down thirty feet. That's an average of one foot a day. Of course, the deeper the hole the more difficult it was

to go down farther. Then imagine their joy when the sand turned black and oil started to flow from the hole! They collected it and found they were getting as much as two barrels a day.

"Then they went across the canyon and started again. Push and pull, push and pull, hour after hour, day after day. Yet not for a moment did they think the work was tiresome. They believed oil was there and they made up their minds to find it.

"A month later they were down about thirty feet again. Once more oil flowed at about two barrels a day. Their hopes rose. They decided to drill yet another well. Push, pull, push, pull, day in, day out. But this time, even at thirty feet, there was no oil. The well was dry. What a disappointment!

"But did they give up? No indeed. They began again. Push, pull, push, pull, day after day, day after day. Thirty feet, sixty feet, a hundred feet. Still no oil. But they would not give up. Two hundred feet. Three hundred feet. Four hundred feet. Still no oil. Yet they did not give up.

"How they did it, I can't imagine," said Father. "It doesn't seem possible with the simple tools they had. But they kept

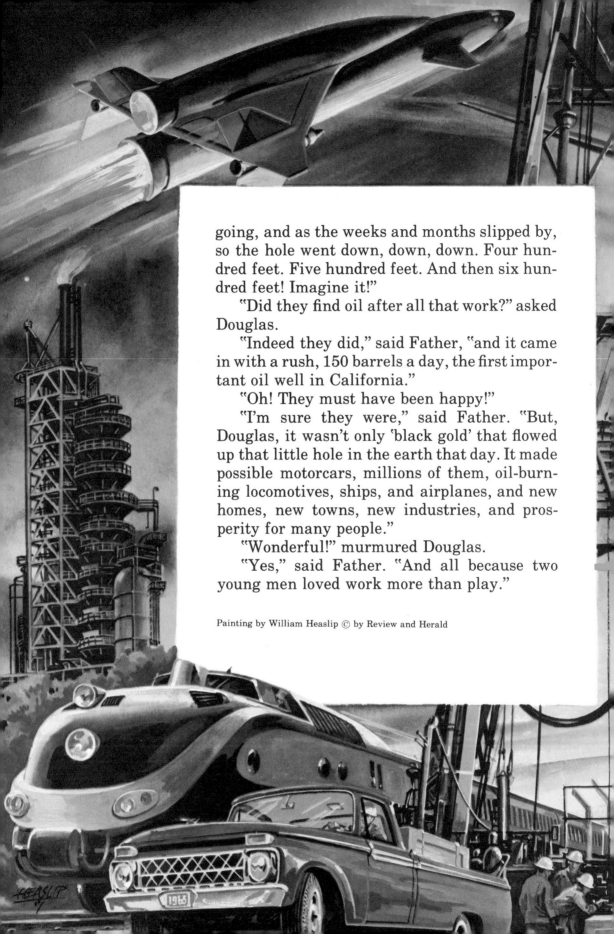

going, and as the weeks and months slipped by, so the hole went down, down, down. Four hundred feet. Five hundred feet. And then six hundred feet! Imagine it!"

"Did they find oil after all that work?" asked Douglas.

"Indeed they did," said Father, "and it came in with a rush, 150 barrels a day, the first important oil well in California."

"Oh! They must have been happy!"

"I'm sure they were," said Father. "But, Douglas, it wasn't only 'black gold' that flowed up that little hole in the earth that day. It made possible motorcars, millions of them, oil-burning locomotives, ships, and airplanes, and new homes, new towns, new industries, and prosperity for many people."

"Wonderful!" murmured Douglas.

"Yes," said Father. "And all because two young men loved work more than play."

Painting by William Heaslip © by Review and Herald

STORY **20**

Why Chrissie Changed Her Mind

"OH, MOTHER," CRIED CHRISSIE, "isn't it lovely to think that I'm really going to get a new dress this week?"

"It surely is," said Mother.

"I think I'll have a green one this time," said Chrissie excitedly. "Then I'll get a brown hat and a little brown handbag. They'll go beautifully with my brown shoes."

"That will be very attractive," said Mother. "And you deserve it, dear. You've been such a good girl, working so hard and saving your pennies as you have. When do you want to go shopping?"

"Just as soon as we can," said Chrissie. "Could we go tomorrow afternoon?"

"I think so. How much money do you have?"

"Nineteen dollars," said Chrissie, opening her purse and counting her precious savings all over again for the twentieth time that day.

"Fine!" said Mother. "I think you have done very well, dear, to save so much. It has meant a lot of hard work. Now you can have the dress you have wanted so long."

94

"I hope we find a nice one," said Chrissie eagerly. "A beautiful pale-green one, with maybe some flowers worked in here and there, don't you think?"

"That might be very pretty," said Mother. "Anyhow, we'll find the best in town."

Chrissie could hardly wait for the time when they were to leave for town, but it came at last. They caught a bus, and away they went.

As the bus stopped here and there on its way to town, Chrissie noticed a big colored picture on the billboards. It showed two ragged children, one with a crutch because he had lost a leg. Above, in big letters, were the words, "Help the Red Cross to Help Them."

"What is that picture about?" asked Chrissie.

"It must be Red Cross day," said Mother. "I had forgotten."

"But the picture," said Chrissie. "What about those poor children."

"Oh," said Mother, "those poor little children represent all the children who are suffering because of wars or earthquakes, or other disasters, around the world. Millions of

them have lost fathers and mothers and, well, everything. It is very, very sad. Now kind people are trying to do all they can to help them."

"Haven't they any food or proper clothes?" asked Chrissie.

"Many of them would starve or freeze to death if it weren't for the Red Cross and other agencies who send help to them."

"I suppose we should help too," said Chrissie.

"Oh, yes, of course, we will," said Mother. "But here is where we get off. The store I want to take you to is just a few yards farther on."

They got off the bus and hurried to the shop.

"There's that picture again," said Chrissie, stopping a moment to look closer at the two ragged children and the crutch.

"Yes, they are all over the place," said Mother. "Now here we are. What do you think of that green dress in the window?"

"It's lovely," said Chrissie, "but it isn't exactly what I want. Let's go inside and look at some more."

They walked over to the elevator.

"They even have that picture in here, Mother," she said as they went up to the fourth floor.

"So they do," said Mother. "I suppose people will give a lot of money to help those poor children today."

Now they were in the dress department and the saleslady was bringing out all the green dresses she had in stock. Chrissie looked them over carefully, enjoying herself no end as she turned from one to the other. But she couldn't tell which one to choose—they were all so beautiful. At last she found one that seemed just right. It was the right color and the right size and the right price—and yet, somehow she couldn't say Yes. Something made her hesitate. She couldn't tell what, or could it be those poor children staring at her from the Red Cross box on the counter? She couldn't forget how sad they looked.

"Mother," she said at last, "I don't think I can decide just now. Let's leave it for a little while and look somewhere else."

"I don't think you'll find a better dress," said Mother, "but it's for you to decide. It's your money."

The saleslady promised to put the dress to one side for an hour or two, and out they went.

"I don't understand you, Chrissie," said Mother. "That dress was the very one you wanted."

But Chrissie didn't seem to hear. Instead she stepped up to a lady in the Red Cross uniform who was standing beside a big picture of the two poor ragged children.

"Do you need a lot of money to help those poor children?" she asked.

"Yes, my dear," said the lady, "we do. There are millions of them all over the world without food or clothing, and we are trying to help as many as we can."

"I would like to give my dress money, if you don't mind," said Chrissie. "You see, I have plenty of old dresses, and I don't really need a new one. And I can save up again, you know."

With that Chrissie opened her purse, drew out her precious dollars, and placed them in the lady's hand.

"Thank you very much," said the lady, with a smile. "God bless you, dear."

Chrissie wondered why there were tears in the lady's eyes. Then she looked up at Mother and saw there were tears in her eyes too.

"Now we can go home again, can't we, Mother?" she said.

"Chrissie," said Mother, "you are the strangest, dearest girl in all the world. Let's catch the next bus."

Chrissie gave dollars, her precious dress money, to the lady in the Red Cross uniform.

STORY **21**

That Pond Again!

IN JOHNNIE'S GARDEN there was a beautiful pond, complete with water lilies, goldfish, and a bridge. Oh, yes, and a waterfall, too; that is, when Daddy turned on the water, for visitors to see.

Winding in and out amid little dwarf trees and bushes, the pond made this part of the garden very pretty indeed; and it was so innocent looking that a stranger would never suspect that boys and girls could get into trouble there.

Not that anybody was likely to drown in it, for it was only a foot deep or something like that; but there are other things that can happen to people in ponds besides getting drowned.

So many things had, in fact, happened at this particular

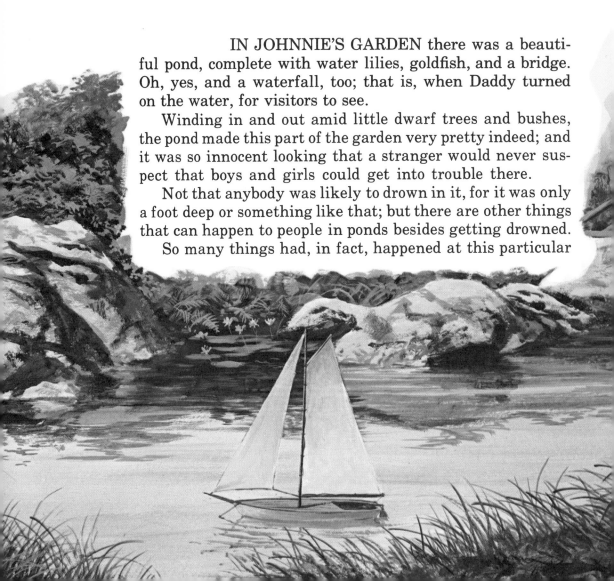

pond that Mother had laid down the law that the children were not to play anywhere near it without her special permission.

"No," she said this very morning; "it's no use coaxing, Johnnie. You cannot play at the pond today. Your clothes are hardly dry from the last time you fell in. What's more, you know Mrs. Norman is coming today with Mary. You must entertain her."

"Is Mary coming today?"

"She is."

"Goody!" cried Johnnie. "Now we'll have some fun."

"But not at the pond," said Mother, "because you will have your best clothes on. So you and Joan keep away from it. See?"

"All right, Mother," said Johnnie, and little Joan echoed, "Awite."

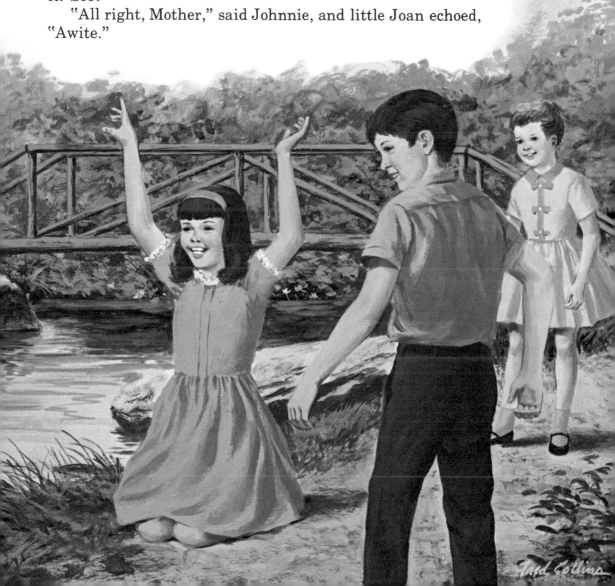

But everything was not "all right," even though Johnnie and Joan said it was. For Mary was a very lively little girl, and as soon as she arrived she cried out in great joy, "Oh, what a lovely pond! Johnnie, let's go and play at the pond!"

Johnnie's sailboat was riding at anchor in one of the little bays, and Mary rushed across the garden toward it. Johnnie followed, with Joan behind him, both of them dressed in their best for Mrs. Norman's benefit.

By the time they reached the pond, Mary was down on her knees, reaching out toward the boat. She wanted to give it a push and send it across the water.

"What a beautiful boat!" she cried. "We can have fun with it."

"I'll get it for you," said Johnnie, picking up a stick—quite forgetting what Mother had said such a little while ago.

"Don't bother," said Mary. "I can reach it. You'll see."

Johnnie did see—and much more than he expected. For Mary, straining to reach the boat, lost her balance and fell flat into the dirty, greenish-looking water!

Right under the water she went, with her nice new shoes, her pretty new dress, and her golden-brown curls. Of course, she didn't stay there very long; just long enough to get herself into a dreadful mess. Then Johnnie, reaching over to lift her out, fell in himself!

What a sight the two made as they walked back to the house, with water running off their hair, dripping from their clothes, and oozing out of their shoes!

If you could have seen Mother's face as she saw them coming! That was a sight too! It said a great many things all at once.

Then came the undressing, or rather the unpeeling, for they were both so wet that their clothes stuck to them like peel on an orange. When their clothes were off, they had to be washed and dried, while Mother hurried around looking for something else for them to wear. Just as they were in the

middle of all this, from far down the garden came the sound of someone screaming.

"Oh, dear, that's Joan!" cried Mother. "Something must have happened to her."

As they all rushed out of the house to find out what was the matter now, they saw a tiny little form trying its best to scramble out of the pond onto the bank! It was Joan. At least, it was all that was left of her and her pretty new dress. She had been trying to pick a water lily and had met the same sad fate as Mary.

Just what Mother's face looked like at this moment nobody could describe. It said even more than it had before.

And when Mrs. Norman and Mary had gone home—Mary in some of Johnnie's old clothes—Mother turned her thoughts into words and actions!

"When I say keep away from the pond," she said, as she shook her finger, "I mean keep away from the pond—no matter who comes to see you, or whatever he or she may say to you."

For some reason that you may guess Johnnie and Joan never disobeyed Mother on this point again.

22

Saved
From the Flood

NIGHT HAD FALLEN. Everybody in the little town was asleep. Everybody, that is, except the policeman, who was keeping his watch all alone in the police station.

Nobody dreamed that danger was near. No serious trouble had come to the town in years and years. There was no sign of trouble now, except that the level of the water in the river was a little higher than usual. But then, the water often rose and fell without anyone's noticing it. Sometimes, especially in the hot, dry summer, the river was merely a little trickle, way down at the bottom of its forty-foot-high banks.

The night wore on. There was no sound save the beating of the rain on the roofs and roadways, and the occasional barking of a dog.

Suddenly the telephone rang sharp and loud in the police station.

Startled a bit, the policeman picked up the receiver. "Hello," he said.

The words that came over the phone shocked him.

"Flood warning!" said a voice. "Lots of water rushing your 105 way. Will reach you in thirty minutes. Get the people out of all houses on low-lying ground. There's no time to lose. Hurry!"

A flood! In thirty minutes! How little time to warn everybody! How quickly he must work!

The policeman sounded the alarm, and in an instant the whole town was alive. A few minutes later men were hurrying to the houses down by the river, waking the sleeping families and helping them move what they could of their goods to higher ground. There just wasn't time to salvage many things.

Some of the people, just roused from sleep, didn't want to move, especially in the middle of the night, with rain pouring down. They couldn't believe that a flood was only a few minutes away. But the policemen and the firemen and other friends hurried them out to safety.

Then it came. About one o'clock in the morning a wall of water, full of uprooted trees, broken houses, and dead animals, rushed by. On its churning surface were tables, chairs, pianos, oil drums, and even cars! It hit the bridge in the middle of town and carried it away as though it had been made of paper. It overflowed its banks and filled all the low-lying land nearby. Some of the houses which people had left but a few minutes before were lifted off their foundations and sent sailing downstream. Others simply collapsed, fell apart, and were carried away.

By this time hundreds of people were standing on high ground near the river, peering through the darkness at the terrible scene before them. How glad they were that nobody was in those houses that were being smashed and carried away by the flood!

"Look!" cried someone, pointing over the swirling water. "Surely that was a light! Over there; look!"

"It can't be," said others. "There's nobody there; and there's no light anyway."

"But there it is again! Look! It must be a candle. Somebody keeps lighting it, and it blows out."

"So it is! You're right. Whose house is it?"

"That's Mrs. Smith's house. Her husband's in the Army, and she had four little children with her. Didn't anybody warn them?"

No, nobody did. Somehow, in the darkness and the excitement, that house had been missed. Now it was surrounded by wild, rushing water which threatened any moment to carry it away.

"Give me a rope!" cried some brave soul. "I'll swim over there!"

They tied a rope round the man, and he set off. But he couldn't get anywhere near. It was impossible. The swift current carried him away, and it was only with great difficulty that he was hauled back. Another man offered to go but he also failed. A third made the attempt, but exhausted, had to give up.

Meanwhile, out there in the darkness a brave mother was making a gallant fight for life and for the lives of her children.

108   As no one had called to warn her of the coming flood, she and her children were all fast asleep when the first rush of water came sweeping into their house. Awakened by shouts and the roar of the flood waters going by, she jumped out of bed, to find herself standing in two feet of water, which covered the bedroom floor and was fast rising. Suddenly realizing what had happened, she grabbed her four children and lifted them one by one onto the top of a large cupboard. Then as the water rose above the beds, the table, the chairs, she clambered up on top of the cupboard herself, taking with her a candle and matches, a dry blanket, a bottle of milk, a knife, an old chisel, and, of all things, a flatiron!

Now they were all huddled together on top of the cupboard, wondering just how high the water would rise. Then it was that this dear, brave mother began to pray that God would spare her and her children, and if not, let them die together.

An hour passed by. Two hours. It was now three o'clock in the morning. They could feel the water close to the top of the cupboard. Suddenly one of the inside walls of the house gave way and fell with a great splash.

"The end must be near now," this brave mother said to herself. But she was not ready to give up yet.

Now it was that she made use of the tools she had so wisely brought with her, thinking that she might in some way need them.

Just over their heads was the ceiling, made of thin boards. "If I could just cut through it," she said to herself, "we could climb up on the rafters. Then we would be another two feet above the water."

Seizing the flatiron and the blunt chisel, she began chipping away at the board, splitting it off in little pieces until she had made a hole two feet long by nine inches wide. Through this tiny hole she pushed her children, one by one, telling each to sit astride a rafter. She was afraid they might

Painting by Harry Anderson © by Review and Herald ▶

Mrs. Smith quickly lifted her four children, one by one, to the top of a large cupboard.

fall through the frail board if they were to stand on it. Then she pulled herself up through the hole and sat with them there, waiting, wondering, praying, while below, the water swirled through the house.

Four o'clock. Five o'clock. Six o'clock. It was getting light now. And what a scene! The great brown torrent was still surging by, with bits of broken houses and furniture floating on its surface.

Hundreds of people who had watched all night were looking anxiously at the one little house still standing in the midst of the flood. Only its roof could be seen now, with the tops of some of its windows. Surely everybody in it must have drowned long ago!

But no! As they look they see that somebody is cutting a hole in the roof!

The brave little mother is making her last attempt to save her children. She apparently is going to lift them out onto the roof if need be!

A shout goes up from the people and tears come to many eyes. But the little family is still in grave danger. At any moment the house could begin to come apart under the pressure of the swirling water.

"Let me try again," says a strong swimmer. "I think I can make it now."

They tie a rope around his waist and he sets off through the raging waters. He is swept downstream, but fights his way up again. At last, after a mighty effort, he reaches the house. Another shout goes up from the people anxiously watching on the bank. He has got there in time! The family may yet be saved.

Tying the rope securely, he makes his way in through a window. The large cupboard, on which the family had waited so long, and by which they had climbed into the loft, is gone. He signals back for a ladder. Soon another swimmer, aided by the rope, is on his way with one. Another swimmer fol-

lows. Soon one of them is seen coming from the house with a
little girl on his shoulders.

Another mighty cheer rends the morning air. Then another and another as one by one the children are brought by strong hands along the rope, strained to the uttermost by the fury of the torrent.

Then, as all brave captains are the last to leave a sinking ship, so this dear mother is the last to leave her falling house. When all her four children have been taken to safety she comes out herself and, with the help of her rescuers, makes her way to land. What a cheer the people give for her! And she deserves it. Brave little mother!

I hope her children never forget how they were saved from death that dreadful night. It was a mother's faith against a flood.

STORY **23**

Vera's Victory

VERA WAS ONE of those very lively little girls—you know the kind. Full of high spirits. Always getting into mischief. The kind that makes Mother tired and gives Father headaches.

This particular afternoon Vera had been a little more lively than usual, and when the time came for her to go to bed no one was more happy than her mother.

"At last!" sighed Mother, as she went downstairs after tucking Vera into bed and kissing her good night. "Now, perhaps, I can have a little peace."

Mother went into the dining room, now quiet and still. Feeling very tired, she decided to lie on the sofa for a little while and take a rest. Gradually she felt herself falling asleep. Then, before her eyes were quite closed, something began to happen.

Very slowly, very softly, the dining room door began to open. A little more, and a little more.

Who could it be? thought Mother, frightened. Had a burglar gotten into the house?

Then, what do you suppose? From behind the door came a

white-robed figure. Yes, it was little Vera in her nightie.

Mother did not move. Nor did she say a word. She just pretended to be asleep, and watched.

Vera tiptoed across the soft carpet over to the dining table.

Now, in the middle of the table was a large bowl of apples, oranges, and nuts. On top of all was a big bunch of grapes. Vera had been looking at this bunch of grapes all day, wishing that it might be hers. Now she reached out her hand, picked up the grapes, and tiptoed out of the room, closing the door very quietly behind her.

Of course she thought that nobody had seen her. But Mother, as usual, had seen everything. Mother always does!

But now Mother felt very sad.

"To think that my Vera would do a thing like that!" she said to herself. "To think that my own little girl would wait till she thought I was not looking and then creep down here

to steal that bunch of grapes! Oh dear, what shall I do? What shall I say to her?"

Then, just as Mother was feeling very much upset, something began to happen again.

Once more the dining room door began to open—very softly, very slowly. From behind it came the same little white-robed figure. It was Vera again, still in her nightie, and still clasping the bunch of grapes tightly in her hand.

Tiptoeing over to the table, she put the bunch of grapes back in exactly the same place that she had found it. Then, in a big, loud voice, she said, "And there, Mr. Devil, that's where you get left."

After that she turned around and started for the door. But before she had reached it, Mother was on her feet and her arms were clasped around Vera's neck.

"Oh, darling!" she cried. "I'm so glad you won the victory over that temptation!"

What a happy time they both had then!

I like to think of what must have happened on the stairs that evening. All the way up, the voice of the tempter had said, "Go on, Vera; grapes have a lovely taste. Take one. Nobody will know. It will be all right. Mother will never find out."

At the same time another voice inside her had said, "No, don't, Vera. That would be stealing. That would be wrong. Mother wouldn't like it. Be a good girl and take those grapes back! Put them back where you found them."

Somewhere on the stairs the victory was won. And after that everything turned out happily—as it always does when we fight temptation and win.

Every boy and girl is tempted at some time or other to do something wrong. Sometimes the temptation is very strong indeed. Sometimes you may wonder what *is* the right thing to do. But if you listen to that little voice that speaks within your heart, the voice of conscience, you will not make a mistake. Jesus will give you the victory, if you ask His help.

STORY **24**

Walter
and the Wolves

WALTER WAS AS EXCITED as a boy could be. Dad was going on a camping trip and had just told him that he could go along too! He always loved to go on trips with his dad, but to go away with him for a whole week—that seemed too good to be true. What's more, they were going to sleep in a tent and cook their own food over a campfire.

The next few days were spent getting everything ready —tent, bedding, cooking outfit, ax, lantern, and all that. As the pile of things grew in the garage, Walter could hardly keep himself from shouting aloud for joy. He was going camping in the mountains with Dad!

At last the great day came. There were four in the party— Dad, two of his friends, and Walter. They packed some of the things in the trunk of the car and the rest they tied on top.

They drove toward the mountains, then up, up, up, curving this way and that through beautiful forests until at last they were so high they were almost above the timber line. Now and then, as they looked down, they caught wonderful views of woodlands, lakes, and rivers far below.

116   At last they came to a beautiful lake hidden deep in the

mountains. This, said Dad, was the place they had been heading for, although the best campsite was on the other side of the water. So they drove the car as far as they could, then unloaded it and carried the things around. At last the tent was set up and a fire lighted to cook the evening meal.

Walter was thrilled. It was all so different and so wonderful. He had never seen anything like it—the stillness of the lake, the sun setting behind the great mountain peaks, the distant sounds of wild animals.

"What's that noise?" he asked Dad. "It sounds like dogs."

"Just wolves," said Dad. "There are lots of them up in these mountains, but they won't bother us. They are a long way off."

Walter tried not to think of the wolves anymore, but now and then he couldn't help wondering a little. They might be a long way off, he thought to himself as he went to sleep that night, but they could come nearer, couldn't they? But there, Dad and his two friends were in the tent with him, so why

118   should he worry? And with this thought he went to sleep.

The next day they were all up early, and set off along the wooded shore of the lake.

What a grand time they had! Walter had never enjoyed himself so much before. He wished he could stay up there in the mountains for the rest of his life. But of course he couldn't.

At last the day came when they must leave the camp. The tent was taken down and all the things were soon packed.

Dad and his friends picked up the bundles and headed back toward the car, with Walter walking beside them.

Presently Dad stopped. "I don't see why we should carry these things all round the end of the lake. Let's cut through the swamp. But it's too deep for Walter. We men will go through the swamp, get the car ready, and Walter can walk round the swamp and meet us on the other side. O.K.?"

"Of course," said Walter, "and I'll be there before you."
The men laughed, for they knew he couldn't do that.

Walter started off, his path leading him through some very wild country. He didn't mind being alone, of course, but he didn't like that sound—that howling of the wolves. Somehow it seemed to be much nearer than Dad had said it was.

He hurried on, determined to get to the car before the others. Pressing his way through low shrubs and clambering over rocks, he reached the end of the lake and started around the other side. Then suddenly he saw something that froze him in his tracks. Running toward him, down the mountainside, was a pack of wolves! There were seventeen of them altogether. Walter counted them, frightened though he was.

They were big, and the sight of them almost made his heart stand still.

There was a big rock nearby, and Walter tried to climb it, hoping to get out of their way. But he couldn't get a foothold, and down he slid again. Now they were nearer, nearer.

I don't know whether they were coming after Walter or not, but he certainly thought they were.

He shut his eyes and prayed. He said, "Dear Lord, don't let those wolves harm me! Please make them go away!"

Those seventeen wolves came within ten feet of him. He

could look right into their eyes, almost down their throats.

Then something happened. "All of a sudden," Walter told me afterward, "those wolves turned tail and ran back up the mountain. What made them do it? Could they have caught a glimpse of my guardian angel?"

"I can't say they didn't," I replied.

When the wolves were gone, Walter went on his way. Soon he was back at the car where Dad and his friends were waiting anxiously for him.

"What kept you?" they asked. "Why did you take so long?"

Then he told them all that had happened. "Jesus heard my prayer just in time," he told them.

Painting by Harry Baerg

25

Impatient Ian

IT WAS ALWAYS hard for Ian to wait for anything. He wanted his breakfast as soon as he got downstairs in the morning. He wanted his dinner the moment he returned from school. And he was always annoyed if anyone kept him waiting.

When his birthday drew near, or Christmas, and he thought he might receive some present he had longed for, well, he just went through agonies. Every day seemed a week, and every week a year. Over and over again he would go to Mother or Father and say, "How much longer do I have to wait?" They would remind him of the date on the calendar, but a little while later he would pop up with the same question.

It was this way when he wanted a new bicycle. Indeed, he nearly drove everybody crazy asking when he was going to get it. Father and Mother almost wished they had never promised him one, he made such a fuss.

After what seemed to Ian a lifetime, the bicycle arrived. For a moment he was contented, admiring its bright-red frame and shiny silver wheels. Then he was impatient to ride

it, and dashed off up the street at full speed. Back and forth, back and forth, he rode, faster and faster, until he was exhausted.

Next morning he rushed downstairs before anyone else in the house was awake, anxious to ride it again. Imagine his disgust and disappointment when he discovered that the front tire was soft!

Feverishly he searched for a pump, but there was none to be found.

"Where's the pump?" he shouted. "Where's the pump? I want the bicycle pump."

Father put his head around his bedroom door.

"What's all this noise about?" he asked.

"My front tire's soft!" cried Ian, almost angrily, as if it were Father's fault.

"Suppose it is," said Father. "That's no reason for waking the whole family at this unearthly hour."

"But I want the pump!" cried Ian. "And I want it right away. I'm going out for a ride."

"The pump's broken," said Father.

"Then what am I going to do? I must have a pump. I want to use my bicycle."

124   "There is no pump," said Father sternly. "So I'm afraid you'll have to wait, or walk down to the gas station and have the man there pump your tire up. And now," he added, closing the door, "let's have a little peace and quiet."

"Walk to the gas station!" Ian muttered to himself. "That will take me fifteen minutes. Why can't there be a pump about when a fellow needs one?"

But there was no use fuming, for Father had disappeared and the house was quiet again. If he wanted an early-morning ride, he would have to walk to the gas station, and this he decided to do.

Ian didn't enjoy that walk. He hated pushing his new bicycle all that way, and he hated what seemed to him a dreadful waste of time. When at last he arrived at the gas station he wasn't at all in a very good frame of mind, as you can imagine.

"Hi!" he called to the attendant, "I want my tire pumped up."

"You'll have to wait a minute, son," said the man. "I have to attend to a customer first. I'll be with you just as soon as I can."

Wait a minute! He couldn't do that. He had been waiting fifteen minutes already. Why didn't the man come at once

when he called him? Why couldn't he leave his customer and do the job for him right away? Telling him to wait a minute indeed!

"I'll do it myself," he said. "I won't 'wait a minute' for him or anybody else."

So Ian hurried over to the place where the air pump was kept, took down the air line and tried to fix the gauge on the valve of his front wheel.

"Better wait for me," called the attendant. "I've just had a new gauge put on and I don't think it registers right. I won't be a minute."

"Won't be a minute!" exclaimed Ian. "You've been five minutes already. I'm not going to wait for you. I can do it myself."

"All right," said the man. "Go ahead."

So Ian squeezed the lever and the air rushed into the tire with a hiss.

"It's easy!" said Ian to himself. "Glad I didn't wait for him."

He was fascinated by the figures on the gauge. Quickly the pressure mounted. Twenty pounds. Thirty pounds. Forty pounds. Fifty pounds. Sixty pounds.

126   If he hadn't been in such a hurry, he would have felt his tire to see how hard it was. And if he had had a little more common sense, he would have known that no bicycle tire could stand much more pressure.

But he went on squeezing the lever. Seventy pounds. Eighty pounds. Ninety pounds!

Suddenly there was a report like a cannon shot, and Ian was shocked to see his beautiful new tire and tube ripped to pieces.

Poor Ian! He was furiously angry, but he didn't know whom to blame, except himself. With tears in his eyes he walked off down the street, pushing his bicycle beside him, and wondering what Father would say to him when he got home.

The attendant, who told me all about it, said that the tire was absolutely ruined. There was nothing he could have done to mend it.

"A new tire, too," he said, "spoiled by impatience."

STORY **26**

The Strange Duet

TUM, TUM, TUM. Tum, tum, tum. Tum, tum—— There was no end to it.

"Oh, can't somebody make that child stop playing the piano!" cried the red-faced old gentleman in the hotel lobby. "I came here for rest and quiet, and all I can hear is 'tum, tum, tum,' all day long."

"It shouldn't be allowed," said another guest. "It's a perfect nuisance."

"I don't know why they keep a piano in the hotel parlor anyway," chimed in a third guest. "It's simply driving me crazy."

"Children should be told to keep quiet," said a fourth guest.

"Why don't they lock the piano?" said a fifth. "Then she couldn't play it."

There was a brief pause as the angry guests tried to think of something else to say about the little girl enjoying herself at the piano.

In the silence they heard it again.

Tum, tum, tum. Tum, tum, tum. Tum, tummety, tum.   127

"Oh!" cried the red-faced gentleman. "I can't stand it. I'm going to complain to the manager."

"Of course," cried the rest. "Why didn't we think of that before? Let's all go to him at once and tell him we'll leave his hotel unless he locks the piano or keeps that girl from pounding on it."

So, in a body, they went to see the manager.

"Whose is that child who makes all that racket on the piano?" cried the angry spokesman.

"Mine," said the hotel manager meekly.

"Then why don't you tell her to stop?" said the man. "She's making our lives unbearable."

"I'm sorry," said the manager. "I should have told her to stop before, of course. But she is not very well, and playing the piano is the one thing that seems to make her happy. She wants to be a good pianist someday. However, she mustn't annoy my guests. I will tell her to stop."

Without another word he walked toward the parlor,

the angry guests following to make sure that he kept his promise.

Suddenly they all stopped. For as the manager opened the parlor door, there came forth such beautiful music as none of them had heard in a long time.

They peered around the door. The little girl was still there at the piano. And she was still playing her favorite little piece. But beside her was someone else, a kindly gentleman with dark clothes and silver gray hair. They recognized him as another guest in the hotel, but never dreamed who he was. Now as he sat beside the little girl he played grand, majestic chords that blended in with her poor little tune and made it beautiful. Then his skilled fingers ran up and down the piano, passing hers this way and that, and producing a beauty and harmony that thrilled her soul with perfect joy.

4-9

This was how she wanted to play! This was the music she was trying to bring from the piano in her poor, humble way! Happy beyond words, she played her piece the best she knew how, and above and through the glorious music of the master could be heard her simple little tune.

Tum, tum, tum. Tum, tum, tum. Tum, tummety tum.

The guests pressed into the parlor. They were not angry now. If anything, they were ashamed. They recognized that, while they had been grumbling and complaining, this other guest, great musician though he was, who might have been most offended by the girl's poor playing, had gone to her help. Wrapping his own great skill around her humble trying, he had made it beautiful.

How often we are like that little girl! Our best efforts to be what we ought to be are so poor, and sometimes so annoying to others. Try as we may, we only get complaints. But somewhere near is the Great Musician, waiting to sit beside us, to use His skill to help us.

"Behold, I stand at the door, and knock," He says.

"Not the door of the parlor. At the door of our hearts. And if we will but let Him in; if we will but say, "Come, Jesus, come and help me play it right," then all our poor, jangling notes will be blended into the glorious harmony He can and will produce in our lives.

Then people will think, "Whatever has happened? You're so different! You're so changed!" And all because we have been with Jesus, and learned of Him.

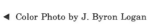
◄ Color Photo by J. Byron Logan

The silver-haired man played majestic chords that blended in with the little girl's tune and made a beautiful harmony.

27

Blackbirds to the Rescue

FARMER JONES WAS FEELING very happy. His tomato plants—twenty-seven acres of them—were all coming along well. Already they were covered with blossoms, with promise of a very large crop.

Looking over the big field, Farmer Jones naturally thought of the harvest, soon to be reaped, and how much he would get for it.

"Those tomatoes mean at least $4,000 to me," he said, "and I hope nothing goes wrong with them; they are all I have."

But even as he spoke an enemy was on the way. It was an army, not of men, but of worms—not really worms, but caterpillars—that move in such large numbers that they are called army worms. They will eat a field clean of every green thing with the speed of locusts.

One morning, as Farmer Jones was walking around his field to see if all was well, he saw the worms in one corner of it, and cold fear seized him. He knew from sad experience that it would be only a matter of days before the pests would

be swarming over all his precious plants and devouring

them. What could he do?

He hurried indoors to tell his wife.

"Come, look, the army worms are here!" he called. "Our crop is lost."

Mother ran out to see, and her heart sank also, for she, too, knew what it meant. The family's living was at stake. Food, clothes, home itself—all depended upon that tomato crop, and now the army worms were eating it up right before their eyes!

Then the children ran out to look, and they were worried, too, for they had worked long hours helping Father to prepare the land, put in all the tomato plants, and irrigate them.

"What are we going to do?" asked Jamey. "We can never kill them all."

"No, we can never kill them all," said Father. "There are too many, and they seem to multiply every minute."

"Father," said Mary, "we must ask Jesus to help us right away."

"Perhaps we should," he said. "But what can He do for us in trouble like this?"

"But doesn't it say somewhere in the Bible, Father, 'I will rebuke the devourer for you'? Why don't we claim that promise?" said Mary.

"Perhaps we should," said Father, "but it's pretty hopeless, now."

"I am going to look it up in the Bible right now," said Mary.

And she did. She found it in the book of Malachi, and read it to the others:

" 'Bring the full tithes into the storehouse, that there may be food in my house; and thereby put me to the test, says the Lord of hosts, if I will not open the windows of heaven for you and pour down for you an overflowing blessing.

" 'I will rebuke the devourer for you, so that it will not destroy the fruits of your soil; and your vine in the field shall not fail to bear, says the Lord of hosts.' Malachi 3:10, 11.

"Fulfill this promise, Lord," they cried. " 'Rebuke the devourer'! Save our tomato fields!"

"There it is, Father," she said eagerly. "I knew it was there. You see now it says that if we are faithful in paying our tithe to God, then God will 'rebuke the devourer' for our sakes. You pay your tithe, Father, so God must do what He says. Maybe He is just waiting for us to ask Him. Why don't we pray right now?"

Somehow the others caught Mary's spirit of faith in the heavenly Father. They knelt down in that tomato field and prayed to God as they had never prayed before, claiming His promised protection.

Father prayed. Mother prayed. The children prayed. They told God how they had tried to be faithful to Him; how they had paid their tithe honestly to His cause to the best of their knowledge and ability, and how they wanted to serve Him loyally all their days. Then they told Him of the terrible thing that was happening to them, and how much they needed His help.

They finished praying and stood up.

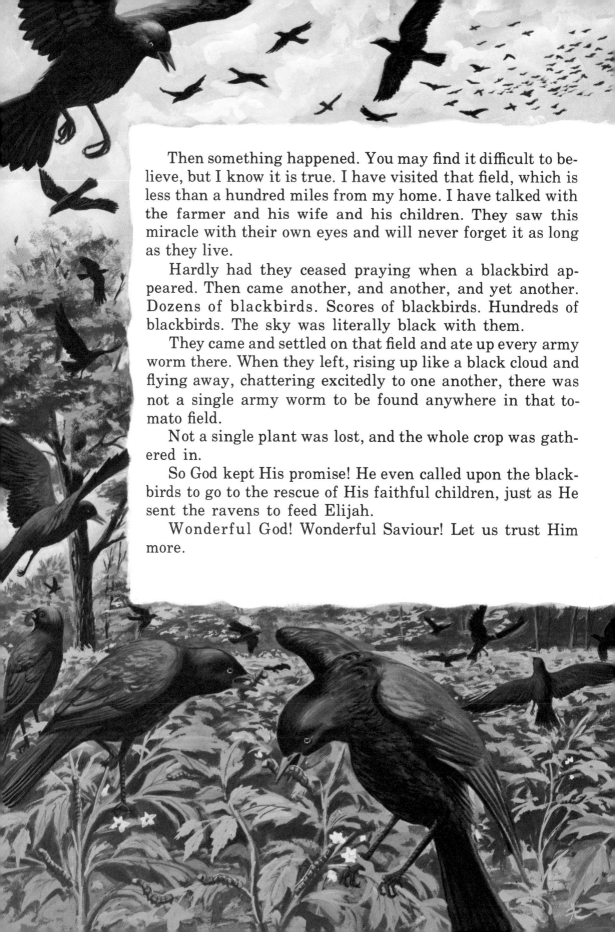

Then something happened. You may find it difficult to believe, but I know it is true. I have visited that field, which is less than a hundred miles from my home. I have talked with the farmer and his wife and his children. They saw this miracle with their own eyes and will never forget it as long as they live.

Hardly had they ceased praying when a blackbird appeared. Then came another, and another, and yet another. Dozens of blackbirds. Scores of blackbirds. Hundreds of blackbirds. The sky was literally black with them.

They came and settled on that field and ate up every army worm there. When they left, rising up like a black cloud and flying away, chattering excitedly to one another, there was not a single army worm to be found anywhere in that tomato field.

Not a single plant was lost, and the whole crop was gathered in.

So God kept His promise! He even called upon the blackbirds to go to the rescue of His faithful children, just as He sent the ravens to feed Elijah.

Wonderful God! Wonderful Saviour! Let us trust Him more.

28

All Over the Bowl

FROM THE TIME that they were little more than babies until now, when they were nearly half grown up —or thought they were—Dudley and Dora had argued over the custard bowl, as to who should scrape it out.

Time and again through the years the same old argument had taken place.

"It's my turn to scrape it."

"No, it's mine."

And nobody ever could remember just whose turn it really was. Usually Mother or Father had to be called upon to decide, and sometimes they guessed right, and sometimes they guessed wrong. Rarely was either of the children satisfied, and I wonder that they didn't keep a record as to who scraped the bowl, and when. It surely would have saved a lot of trouble.

There was something special about this bowl. It had been in this English family for at least thirty years. All the big children who had grown up and gone away from home had scraped it and licked it and quarreled over it. Perhaps that's why it was so very precious in Mother's eyes. Certainly cus-   137

138 tard never tasted right unless it was made in this particular bowl.

When one day, years ago, the bowl had cracked as the hot milk was poured over the custard powder in it, everybody felt sad. But somehow it held together, despite the crack, as though it wanted to go on being the custard bowl for the family till all the children had grown up.

Then it came Christmas time again, and, of course, there had to be custard with the plum pudding. But just as soon as the bowl appeared on the table, the old argument began, even on Christmas Day.

"It's my turn to scrape it out after dinner this time," said Dudley.

"It's mine, and you know it is," retorted Dora.

"No, it isn't."

"Yes, it is."

"Can't you two settle this thing without a squabble today of all days?" said Mother. "Let's hear no more about it, or you'll spoil our Christmas dinner."

So the matter was dropped, and seemingly forgotten; but as the custard got lower and lower in the bowl, toward the end of the dessert, both Dudley and Dora began to eye it with renewed interest.

Now you would think that two usually sensible children, having just eaten a big Christmas dinner, and being about as full as they could be, would take not the slightest interest in the scrapings of a custard bowl. But then, nobody could understand the effect of that particular custard bowl on Dudley and Dora.

No sooner had Mother and Father left the table and gone into the living room than the argument started again.

"It's mine," said Dudley, "so don't let's have any fuss about it."

"It's mine, I tell you," said Dora, holding firmly on to the bowl. "You know very well you scraped it out last time we had custard."

"I didn't."

"You did."

"Well, *I* am going to have it this time," said Dudley, grabbing the bowl with one hand and his spoon with the other.

"No, you are not; I am," said Dora, also seizing the bowl and trying to get her spoon in as well.

Then it happened. Oh, tragedy of tragedies! In the struggle they pulled a little too hard, and the dear old custard bowl broke in two.

Dudley and Dora stood there silent for a moment, holding the broken pieces in their hands, while the custard they were fighting for dropped like little yellow tears on the floor. They were too shocked to speak. They had argued over the bowl many, many times, but they never dreamed it would ever break like this.

Then in one breath they exclaimed, "Oh, dear, what will Mother say?"

You can guess what she said, for she was very sad about it. Indeed, it almost spoiled her Christmas Day.

"I hope this will be a lesson to both of you," she said finally. "What did you gain by quarreling over the bowl? Nothing. You even lost the little bit of custard that was in it. How much better it would have been if one of you had said, 'You may have it this time.' How much happier you would have been! How much more like the Christmas spirit we talk about! Then I wouldn't have lost my bowl."

Somehow the breaking of that dear old bowl did something to Dudley and Dora. They couldn't get it out of their minds, the way it had come apart in their hands, and what a pity it was that something so precious to everybody in the family had been spoiled by their foolish quarrel.

They were much nicer to each other after that. And then —and I must tell you this—when Mother's birthday came round, there was a lovely big box on her plate, marked, "With special love from Dudley and Dora."

Inside was another custard bowl. Not the same as the one that was broken, of course, for that could never be replaced; but one just as near like it as Dudley and Dora could find. Mother kissed them for it and said how pleased she was that they had bought it for her. And if she didn't go and drop a tear right in the middle of it!

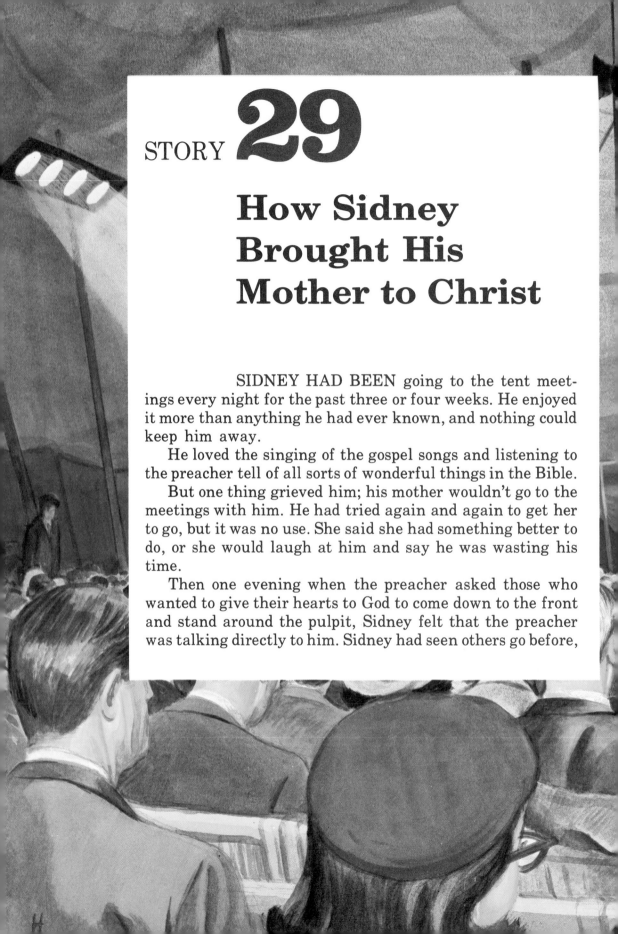

STORY **29**

How Sidney Brought His Mother to Christ

SIDNEY HAD BEEN going to the tent meetings every night for the past three or four weeks. He enjoyed it more than anything he had ever known, and nothing could keep him away.

He loved the singing of the gospel songs and listening to the preacher tell of all sorts of wonderful things in the Bible.

But one thing grieved him; his mother wouldn't go to the meetings with him. He had tried again and again to get her to go, but it was no use. She said she had something better to do, or she would laugh at him and say he was wasting his time.

Then one evening when the preacher asked those who wanted to give their hearts to God to come down to the front and stand around the pulpit, Sidney felt that the preacher was talking directly to him. Sidney had seen others go before, and had wondered why. But this was different. This was for him. This was his night. So he rose, walked to the front, and stood with the others while the preacher prayed earnestly for them.

How he wished his mother were standing with him, giving her heart to God too!

Then he got an idea. If Mother wouldn't come to hear the preacher, maybe the preacher would go to see her. He decided to ask him.

So when the meeting was over, and the preacher had finished talking to all the big people, Sidney went up to him.

"May I speak to you, sir?" he said.

"Surely," smiled the preacher. "What's on your heart, my boy?"

"It's my mother," he said. "I want her to come to the meetings, but she won't come. She thinks I'm stupid for coming.

Painting by William Hutchinson

You see, sir, Mother isn't what she used to be. She doesn't pray anymore. She never reads her Bible. She reads bad stories instead. And she uses bad language sometimes, and I don't like to hear her. She goes out at night, I don't know where, but sometimes I'm afraid she's drinking, sir. Oh, sir, she just isn't what she used to be."

"I'm sorry," said the preacher. "I wonder what we can do for her."

"That's it, sir. That's why I came to talk to you. I just wondered whether you would go to see her."

"I will be glad to," said the preacher. "But, Sidney, there's something I want you to do first."

"Yes, what is it? What can I do?"

"I want you to tell your mother just what you have told me."

"You mean——"

"Yes, everything. Tell her how she has changed, how different she is, and how sad it has made you. It may do more than anything I could say to her."

Sidney thought it over. How could he do it? How could he
speak to his mother like this? But he decided he would try.

"I'll do it," he said.

"It's a promise," said the preacher. "I'll be praying for you."

That night Sidney stayed up later than usual, trying to find a way to begin. But it was hard.

Presently Mother said, "Why don't you go to bed, Sidney?"

"Oh, Mother," began Sidney.

"Go to bed!"

"Yes, Mother," but Sidney still lingered.

"Well, why don't you go?"

"O Mother," said Sidney, with tears in his voice, and going over close to her. "What is the matter? You're not what you used to be. You never say prayers with me anymore. You never read the Bible to me. You never go to church with me. You——"

"Now stop talking that way," said Mother. "And take

146   that," she added, slapping him on the face. "Now go to bed and don't let me hear any more of this sort of talk. So there. Go!"

Sidney went to bed. He felt very sad, but at least he had done his best, and kept the promise he had made to the preacher.

Meanwhile Mother sat quite still, thinking over what Sidney had said. She hadn't meant to slap him. She was sorry about that. And, of course, the boy was right. She wasn't what she used to be. How different! She used to be so happy, but now she was miserable, always miserable and wretched. And Sidney had noticed it. He wanted her to be as she had been once, before she started to drift away from God, before she started to go to the movies all the time, and drink and smoke. He was right. Of course he was right! She ought to go back and start again. It was the only way.

Presently Sidney, lying awake in bed, heard footsteps on the stairs. "It's Mother," he said to himself, "coming to slap me again, I suppose, for talking to her that way."

But it wasn't Mother. At least, it wasn't the mother he had known all these sad weeks and months. It was his own dear mother again, the one he knew and loved so much. And she dropped on her knees beside his bed and burst into tears. Sidney jumped out of bed and knelt beside her.

"I know I'm not what I used to be, Jesus," she sobbed, "but from tonight, with Thy help, I will be."

From that moment everything was different. The old happiness returned. They went to the meetings together and gave their hearts to God again. And Sidney rejoiced that Jesus had helped him say the right thing to his mother that evening.

Painting by Harry Anderson © by Review and Herald ▶

When his own dear mother dropped on her knees and burst into tears, Sidney jumped out of bed and knelt beside her.

30

Hold Up
Your Hand

LARRY WAS SPENDING the summer with his cousin Jack on Grandmother's ranch in Colorado. How they both loved the clear skies, the brilliant sunshine, and all the fun of the farm!

At the bottom of the low hill on which the farmhouse stood ran an irrigation canal, one of those man-made rivers that carry water from the snow-clad Rockies to distant parts of the State where the land is dry and the rainfall meager. Here Larry and Jack played by the hour, sometimes launching little boats and watching them go bobbing down the swiftly running stream; sometimes just sitting on the bank with their feet dangling in the cool, refreshing water.

Unfortunately, neither of the boys could swim, and Grandmother had laid down the law in no uncertain tones that on no account were they to swim in the canal. Of course the boys didn't like this; they thought that it would be quite all right "just to have a dip," even though they couldn't swim. Sometimes they tried to argue with Grandmother about it.

"Why can't we swim a little near the bank?" pleaded Larry.

148

"Because the canal is deep, and if you were to slip you would get out of your depth and you'd never get back."

"Oh, we would!" urged Larry. "I can swim enough for that."

"But you don't understand," said Grandmother. "That water is running more swiftly than you think, and it would carry you down to the sluice before either one of you could struggle out."

"The sluice!" cried Larry. "Why, that's a quarter of a mile away. I could easily struggle out before I got there. Anyway, we wouldn't go into the middle of the canal. All we want to do is to go in close by the bank."

"No!" said Grandmother firmly. "It is too dangerous. If you were both strong swimmers, it would be different. But until you can swim, don't go into the canal. You might find yourselves churned up in the pump."

"The pump? What pump?" asked Larry.

"That sluice carries much of the water into a powerful pump, which lifts it up to irrigate higher ground. Once in there you'd not have much chance to get out alive."

Larry was quite sober for a minute. He didn't like the idea of being churned up in a pump. It sent cold chills down his spine.

But the scare didn't last long.

The day was hot. A cloudless sky left the summer sun free to blaze pitilessly upon the whole parched countryside.

Naturally enough Larry and Jack turned toward the canal as the coolest place they could find. Too hot to launch their little boats, they just lay on the bank looking up into the sky, with their legs trailing in the water.

Presently Larry sat up, a look of determination on his face.

"I don't care what Grandmother says," he burst out, removing his last remaining garment. "I'm going in."

"Better be careful," warned Jack.

"I'll be careful," said Larry, "but I'm going to be cool. If Grandmother were as hot as I am, she'd go in here, too."

With that he flopped into the water with a big splash.
"Come on, Jack!" he cried. "It's wonderful!"

"No," said Jack, "I don't think I'll come. Grandmother wouldn't be pleased."

"Oh, pshaw!" cried Larry. "She's never been in herself, so she doesn't know. It's perfectly safe. And boy, is it cool!"

It looked safe enough; and it was, near the bank. But Larry, his courage growing, began to walk about in the canal. Little by little he went farther from the bank.

"Don't go too far!" cried Jack.

"Oh, it's all right!" cried Larry, splashing about happily. "Come on in, Jack! Why be hot when you don't have to be?"

"But Grandmother——" began Jack.

"Grandmother!" cried Larry. "If only Grandmother would come in she'd—— Oh!"

Then he was gone.

One step too far had carried him to the deep part of the canal, and with hardly a splash he had vanished. When at last he came to the surface he was already many yards downstream.

Jack, horrified, began to shout at the top of his voice.

"Larry's in the canal! Larry's drowning! Grandmother, Grandmother! Come quick! Come quick!"

But Grandmother was too far away and didn't hear him.

Meanwhile Larry, hardly able to keep his head above water, was struggling to get back to the bank. But he couldn't make it. He had never dreamed the current was so strong.

Then he remembered the warning about the sluice, and a new terror seized him. If his hair had not been so wet it would have stood on end.

The roar of the water pouring into the sluice was getting louder, nearer. Swiftly he was being rushed toward it. Beyond it was the pump. How would it feel to be churned up in that pump?

"Help! Help!" he screamed.

Then, looking up into the sky, away beyond the sun, and lifting one hand out of the water, he cried, "Jesus, save me! Jesus, save me!"

At this moment a neighbor working in his field nearby heard the frightened cry. Looking up from his work, he saw an upstretched hand in the canal. At once he guessed what was the matter. Dropping everything, he rushed to the bank.

Bobbing up and down in the water was a head, a boy's head, and it was being carried swiftly toward the sluice, now barely fifty yards away.

The neighbor started to run along the bank. He dared not jump in, for he knew the rushing water would quickly carry both to certain death. There was but one chance. The bridge!

He spurted forward.

"Hold up your hand!" he cried. "I'm making for the bridge. Hold up your hand as you go under!"

Reaching the bridge, the neighbor flung himself down near the spot where the bobbing head would pass underneath. Then he reached down as far as he could; but it was not far enough.

"Hold up your hand!" he cried again.

Wearily, as if with his last ounce of strength, Larry raised his hand.

The neighbor grasped it and dragged the boy to safety.

What a close call that was! Larry never forgot it. He learned a great lesson in obedience that day. He learned, too, that it is always wise to respect the experience of older people. But, best of all, he learned that in times of danger and trial, if you lift up your hand and call on Jesus for help, He will come to the rescue.

Boys and girls, if you should ever be in great peril, or find yourself being swept away by some swift torrent of sin, hold up your hand! Jesus will reach down from above, take your hand in His, and lift you at once to safety.

◄ Painting by William Dolwick

Reaching the bridge, the neighbor flung himself down and grasped Larry's uplifted hand just as he was about to pass under.

The
Tearless Land

I SUPPOSE EVERYBODY cries sometimes. Little boys cry when they are spanked and little girls cry when they are disappointed. Even Mothers and Fathers cry now and then, I believe, when they are very, very upset.

But someday there will be a land where nobody will ever cry again. It seems almost too good to be true, but it is really so. There will be a tearless land where everyone will be supremely happy. Sweet smiles and joyous laughter will light up their faces every moment, and nothing will ever again dim their happiness.

Jesus Himself tells us about this glorious place. "In my Father's house," He says, "are many rooms. . . . And when I go and prepare a place for you, I will come again and will take you to myself, that where I am you may be also." John 14:2, 3, R.S.V.

When His gospel has been taken to every "nation and tribe and tongue and people," He will return, gather His children together—children of every race and nation—and take them with Him to heaven.

154   In heaven those who have been separated by death—

Painting by Peter J. Rennings © by Review and Herald ▶

In that beautiful heavenly land Jesus will be with us. There will be no crying or pain.

156   brothers and sisters, mothers and fathers, who have believed in Jesus—will then meet never to part again.

And then, after a long, happy time in the Holy City in heaven, the earth will be made over. "I saw a new heaven and a new earth," writes John the apostle, "and I saw the holy city, new Jerusalem, coming down out of heaven from God. . . . [And] he will wipe away every tear from their eyes, and death shall be no more, neither shall there be mourning nor crying nor pain any more, for the former things have passed away." Revelation 21:1-4, R.S.V.

What will it be like on the new earth, that tearless land? Certainly it will be peaceful. There will be no quarrels there. Even the animals will stop fighting. "The wolf and the lamb shall feed together, the lion shall eat straw like the ox. . . . They shall not hurt or destroy in all my holy mountain, says the Lord." Isaiah 65:25.

There will be plenty to eat there. Boys and girls who never had enough to eat before will find that Jesus has an endless supply of good things. "They shall hunger no more, neither thirst any more. . . . For the Lamb [Jesus]. . . will guide them to springs of living water." Revelation 7:16, 17.

Jesus will provide the best of everything for all His children. Everybody will be happy. No one will ever cry.

Won't that be a lovely home? Doesn't it make you want to live there with Jesus?

Jesus is coming back soon to take us all there, if we trust in Him and if we let Him give us new hearts and make us ready to meet Him. (Read the story "New Hearts for Old" in Volume I.)

STORY **32**

The Mystery of the Silver Dollar

MANY YEARS AGO, about 1896 or 1897, a Bible colporteur was walking down Market Street in San Francisco when a stranger stopped him and asked him why he did not take his Bibles and books to a certain valley beyond Sacramento.

The colporteur explained that he had never heard of the valley, but would be glad to go as soon as his work was finished in San Francisco. Then the stranger bade him good-by, and disappeared in the crowd.

"That's strange!" the colporteur said to himself. "I wonder why that man spoke to me? How did he know my business? And why is he interested in that particular valley? I must try to go there someday."

But weeks slipped by before the colporteur set forth on his journey, taking his Bibles and other books with him. It was a long and tiring trip, for there were no autos in those days. Part of the way he went by train, part on horseback, part on foot. When he came to the valley he saw houses on the other side of a river, but there was no bridge. As he wondered how he was going to get to the other side, a man appeared in a

157

"Yes," said the colporteur. "How much will you charge to take me over?"

"A dollar," was the reply. That was high, but the colporteur agreed since he hoped to make several sales of his books on the other side.

On the way across, while talking to the boatman, the colporteur brought out a silver dollar. He looked at it with more than usual care because it was a new 1896 coin, bright from the mint, but marred by a scratch on the eagle.

Arriving at the other side, the colporteur gave the boatman the silver dollar and bade him good-by.

"Be sure to call at that house up on the hill there," said the boatman, pointing toward a cottage on a hillside about a mile or so away.

Some time later, as the colporteur came near the hillside cottage, the front door opened and three children ran down the hill toward him. "Did you bring our Bible?" they cried. "Did you bring our Bible?"

"Your Bible!" he exclaimed. "What do you mean? How did you know I have some Bibles?"

"Oh," they cried, "we've all been praying for a Bible, but Mother didn't have the money to buy one till today. But God sent her the money, so we felt sure He would send us the Bible soon."

By this time they were at the house, and the mother was there, standing at the door all flushed and excited, waiting to tell the stranger her story.

"It's true," she said. "We have wanted a Bible so long. We've been praying for one for many months, but somehow could never afford it. Then only a little while ago, after we had all prayed again, a voice seemed to say to me, Go and look outside the front door. So I went out and there, lying on the ground, in front of the house, was a silver dollar. I felt sure God had answered our prayer, and that the Bible

◀ Painting by Vernon Nye

As he waited at the water's edge, a man appeared in a rowboat and asked if he wished to cross.

would come soon. Sir, do you have a Bible for a dollar?"

"I do," he said. "Here's one for just a dollar."

Opening his case he took out a Bible and handed it to the mother, who in turn passed over to him the dollar she had found that very afternoon.

Now it was the colporteur's turn to be astonished as he looked at the coin. It was newly minted, but had a scratch on the eagle. And the date was 1896!

"Is anything wrong with it?" asked the mother anxiously.

"No, no," he said. "But, madam, this is the identical dollar I gave to the man who rowed me across the river this very afternoon!"

"That is strange. I don't know who it could have been," said the woman.

"Someone must have wanted you to have that dollar," said the colporteur.

The mystery of that silver dollar will perhaps never be solved. But both the colporteur and that godly woman were convinced, as I am, that God was in this thing. He knew of the longing of that family to read His Word; and in His own wonderful way He answered their prayer and made it possible for them to receive it.

The Last Leaf on the Tree

"NOW, FRANCIS, LET'S GO into the dining room and play some games," said Freda to her little guest.

It was Freda's birthday, and she had invited Francis, the boy who had just come to live next door, to have lunch with her.

"Let's play the games in the kitchen," suggested Francis. "Let's not go into the dining room."

"But why?"

"Because the old lady is in there," said Francis, "and——"

"The 'old lady'!" exclaimed Freda. "Why, that's my grandma—my mother's grandma, really."

"Oh," said Francis, "but won't she grumble if we make a noise?"

"Oh dear no!" said Freda. "You don't know Grandma; she loves to have us play where she is. You come and see."

So they went into the dining room, and Freda introduced Francis to Grandma. She greeted him with such a cheery smile that his fears were banished at once.

"You don't mind our playing in here, do you, Grandma?" said Freda.

161

"Mind?" echoed Grandma. "I'd mind if you didn't. I love to see you play. It makes me feel young again myself."

So with Mother's help the children were soon having great fun playing blindman's buff, hunt the thimble, and all the other games that children love to play at birthday parties. Grandma joined in as best she could from the security of her armchair, and didn't mind the noise a bit, not even when Freda as "blindman" chased Francis round and round her chair.

At last the children grew tired of their frolic, and came to sit down by the fire at Grandma's knee.

"Tell us a story, Grandma," begged Freda. "You have such lovely stories to tell."

"A story?" questioned Grandma. "What shall it be about this time?"

"About when you were a little girl," suggested Freda, who never seemed to grow tired of listening to Grandma on this subject.

"That was a long, long time ago," said Grandma, "but I still remember some of the things I used to do when I was young. I've told you lots about them before, but there's one thing I was especially thinking about this afternoon before you children came in."

"Do tell us about that, then," said Freda eagerly.

"I'm afraid it isn't a real story," replied Grandma, "and it is a little sad."

"That is all the better," answered Freda, making herself a little more comfortable. "I like sad stories best of all."

"Then I will tell you," said Grandma. "As I was sitting here this afternoon, I began to think of all the little children I used to know when I was a little girl, and of my own brothers and sisters."

"Did you have brothers and sisters?" asked Freda. "I never knew that."

"Why, yes," said Grandma. "And we all loved one another very much. We had a dear mother and were such a happy family. We went to school together—such as it was—and we loved to romp and play just as you do. Times were harder in some ways then, and we didn't have the comforts that folks have nowadays, but we got a good deal of joy out of life."

Grandma paused and sighed a little as her mind went back over the days that were gone forever. Then she went on.

"The years have rolled by very quickly, but as they have passed I have seen all the little children who were with me in school grow up from boys and girls to manhood and womanhood. I went to many of their weddings, and afterward, when they became daddies and mommies, I loved to play with their children. Still the years passed, and they have grown tired and fallen asleep. Gradually, as in the autumn time the old leaves fall from the trees, so they too have passed away. I was

Photo by Dick Dower

thinking this afternoon that of all our happy little group of children in the old schoolhouse I alone am left. And there came back to my mind that beautiful verse of the poet:

> " 'If I should live to be
> The last leaf on the tree
>   In the spring,
> You may laugh, as I do now,
> At the old, forsaken bough,
>   Where I cling.' "

Again Grandma paused. The children were silent, and there were tears in Freda's eyes.

"Grandma mustn't feel lonely," she said lovingly.

"Oh, no," said Grandma bravely. "I am not a bit. That is why I'm so glad to have you come and play around me. *You* wouldn't let anyone get lonely."

Just then there was a knock at the front door. It was someone to say that it was time Francis came home because it was his bedtime.

On the way out to the hall Francis whispered in Freda's ear, "I'm glad we didn't stay in the kitchen for our games, aren't you?"

"Yes," said Freda. "Isn't Grandma beautiful? It would be too bad to make her feel she wasn't wanted, wouldn't it?"

"Yes," said Francis. "I'm coming to see her again, if it's O.K."

And perhaps there are some other old folks here and there who are thinking about the last leaf on the tree and secretly longing for the touch of sympathy and love that you can give.

Spot's New Collar

SPOT WAS JUST an ordinary little wire-haired terrier, but he was the joy of Bobby's heart.

From the moment that Daddy had brought him home as a very tiny puppy for Bobby's birthday present, the two had been the best of friends.

Of course if Bobby had had a baby brother or a baby sister perhaps Spot wouldn't have meant so much to him, but as he didn't have either, and was an only child, why, Spot took all the love he had.

They had such happy, rollicking times together; and Bobby taught him to do tricks, as well as to behave as all well-bred dogs should. He even trained him to be friendly with puss and let her into his kennel.

Then one sad day Spot disappeared.

He just vanished, and no one knew where he was.

When Bobby came home from school and heard the news, a terrible fear gripped his heart.

Spot gone! Then, of course, he must have been run over and killed, as so many, many other poor little dogs are in these days of speeding cars.

But no one around had seen or heard of an accident.

Perhaps someone had stolen him. But how? And when? And why would anybody want to steal such a plain little terrier as Spot?

Poor Bobby was heartbroken. He ran up and down the street calling upon all the neighbors, asking if they had seen his pet, but all replied in the same way. They were very, very sorry, but they had not seen him.

It was a long-faced little boy that came home that night. Bobby had walked miles, asking and searching everywhere, but with no result.

"Don't worry so," said his mother. "Perhaps he will come home in the morning."

Bobby hoped so, but when he rushed out to the kennel soon after sunrise next day, no Spot was there.

"Where can he be?" Bobby asked himself frantically.

"And he'll starve to death without me to feed him. See, here's his supper all untouched."

All day long Bobby worried, and when evening came again, with no sign or sound of Spot, he was ready to cry.

"Isn't there anything else we can do, Mom?" he sobbed.

"Nothing, I'm afraid," said Mother, "except to ask Jesus to help us find him."

Bobby had never prayed so hard and so earnestly as he prayed that night; and the next day he did a very strange thing.

All on his own, and without telling anyone, he opened his little money box, took out all his savings—which amounted to nearly three dollars—and set off downtown on a mysterious errand.

By and by he returned, and entering through the back door, ran right into Mother.

"Why, my dear!" she exclaimed. "Where have you been? And what in the world have you there? Such a beautiful collar and chain. Why——"

Bobby blushed, and was almost ready to cry again, but

through the mist in his eyes he looked up at Mother, and said
quietly, "I bought them for Spot."

"For Spot!" exclaimed Mother. "But poor Spot's gone and maybe——"

"But, Mom," said Bobby reproachfully, "we've asked Jesus to send him back, haven't we?"

"Yes, I know we have, but suppose——"

"Mom," said Bobby, "I believe Jesus is going to answer my prayer anyway and send him back. And I've just spent all my money, every bit I had, on buying this collar and chain so Jesus would see I really believe He will send Spot back again."

Mother threw her arms around Bobby and shed some big tears down the back of his neck. "Why, I'm sure Jesus will send him back."

"I know He will," said Bobby, with the faith of a little child.

One week passed. Two weeks. Three weeks. Four weeks. Five weeks. Yes, five whole weeks, and still there was no sign of Spot!

Mother had quite given up hope. Daddy was talking about buying Bobby another dog, and even Bobby's faith was beginning to waver.

Then very early one morning Bobby was aroused by a familiar sound. It was the barking of a dog—right underneath his window.

He jumped out of bed in a flash, and rushed wildly downstairs.

Yes! Spot was home again. What joy!

And if you could have seen Spot in that fine new collar, with Bobby holding the bright new chain, and the two of them strutting down the street together! No king in his palace was ever happier than they.

35

"All Wrapped Up"

AGNES THOUGHT SHE NEVER would get all her presents wrapped for Christmas. There was one for Daddy and one for Mother; one for Big Sister and one for Little Sister; one for Big Brother and one for Little Brother; one for Uncle John and one for Aunt Jane; and several more for her school friends.

She had bought some pretty paper and some lovely ribbon for the job, but now she was getting impatient. It was taking longer than she had expected.

"Oh dear!" she cried. "Why do we have to wrap presents, anyway?"

"Because they look so much nicer when they're wrapped," said Mother.

"I think we could give the presents just as well without any wrappings," said Agnes.

"We could," said Mother, "but it wouldn't be quite the same. Just think what the living room would be like on Christmas morning if none of the gifts were wrapped! It would look like a bargain counter clearance sale in a department store."

171

"But, Mother, couldn't it save lots of time and money? After the presents are opened they'll just throw away the wrapping anyway."

"True. But the wrapping is part of the gift. It tells of the loving thought that goes with it."

"Maybe so," said Agnes. "But I don't see it. It's going to take me all afternoon to wrap these gifts and the paper will all be torn off and thrown away in ten minutes on Christmas morning."

"But the memory will remain," said Mother, "and after all, it's memories that matter. Isn't that so?"

"Memories! I guess you're right. I never thought of that," said Agnes.

"People not only remember *what* you give them but *how* you give it," said Mother. "If you were to throw a present at someone, or dump it in his lap, it wouldn't mean quite the

same as if you were to hand it to him graciously with kind   173
words and beautiful wrapping."

"Umph," said Agnes as she thought that over. She began
to see the difference.

"By the way," said Mother, "did you know, or perhaps you
have forgotten, that the most precious gift ever given in this
world came 'all wrapped up'?"

"What gift?"

"Jesus, of course," said Mother. "You remember those
lovely words, 'God loved the world so much that he gave his
only Son.'" John 3:16, N.E.B.*

"Yes."

"Well, the Bible says that when the angel told the shep-
herds the Baby Jesus had arrived, he said they would find
Him ' "lying *all wrapped up,* in a manger." ' " Luke 2:12,
N.E.B.*

"Who wrapped Him up?"

"Mary, of course," said Mother. "And I am sure she used
the nicest piece of cloth she had. And when the shepherds arrived at the stable and looked in, they thought this was the
loveliest Baby they had ever seen. Indeed they were so happy
that I am sure they sang about Him all the way back to
their flocks."

"But why was He the best gift anyone ever gave?" asked
Agnes.

"Because, in a way too wonderful for us to understand,"
said Mother, "God Himself was ' "all wrapped up" ' in that
Baby. All His love, all His wisdom, all His power, all His
kindness, all His tenderness, all His compassion.

"Here was a mighty magnet, powerful enough to draw all
men back to goodness and holiness, ' "all wrapped up" ' in
that Baby.

* *The New English Bible,* New Testament. © The Delegates of the
Oxford University Press and the Syndics of the Cambridge University
Press 1970. Reprinted by permission.

Painting by Martin Feuerstein ▶

**In a way too wonderful for us to understand,
God was "all wrapped up" in that Baby of Beth-
lehem.**

"Here was a light of such brightness that it would shine into a thousand million hearts and lead all men—all who would follow it—out of darkness into eternal day; and it was ' "all wrapped up" ' in that Baby.

"Here was a fountain of strength, enough for every human need, that could make the weakest strong and brave and good—and it was ' "all wrapped up" ' in that Baby.

"Here also was a boundless store of hope and courage and beautiful thoughts that would help people make the most of their lives, here and hereafter—and it was ' "all wrapped up" ' in that Baby.

"What a precious package that was! Though nearly two thousand years have passed since it was given to the world, people haven't forgotten it, and they never will. The Bible says, 'to *us* a child is born, to *us* a son is given.' So He belongs to *us.*"

36

The Boy Who Saved the Pilgrims

SUCH A FUNNY name he had! Not George or Henry or Tommy, but Squanto. Imagine giving a boy a name like that! But then, you see, he was an Indian.

As a boy Squanto grew up in a beautiful land of forests and streams which later became known as New England. All his friends were Indians. Now and then he had seen white people, but he did not like them. In fact, he was afraid of them. They were cruel. They came in big ships, with lots of sails, and they would come ashore shooting, looting, and kidnaping people to take away as slaves.

Whenever Squanto saw one of the white man's ships anchor offshore, he would hide in the woods. But one day he too was caught and, with several other Indians, was carried away to a place the white men called England. That was in the year 1605, and for nine years Squanto did not see his home or his people again.

Those were sad years for Squanto. How he longed for his home! All the time he kept thinking how he might get back there again. Then, in 1615, finding a ship bound for America, he arranged with the captain to put him off as close as possi-

177

ble to where he used to live.

How happy he was to be home again, to see his friends and the place he loved so well! But his happiness did not last long. Only a few months later he was kidnaped again and, after another long trip to Europe, sold into slavery at Malaga, in Spain.

Determined to get back to his native country, he escaped and got on board a ship that was sailing for England. Finally, after many adventures, he reached America once more.

But only a little while later, in 1618, he was kidnaped again and taken to England. So great was his longing for home, however, that he again escaped from his captors. By the following summer he was back in New England. This time, however, there was no glad homecoming. No one was there to greet him. Everybody was dead. All his relatives and friends, his whole tribe, had been wiped out by a pestilence. He was the sole survivor.

If anybody had good reason to hate white people, surely it was Squanto. Yet it was he who showed them the greatest kindness in their time of need.

One day—it was December 26, 1620—another ship anchored in the bay near his home. Indians watched anxiously from the shelter of the trees. Perhaps Squanto watched too. Again white men were coming. But they had women and children with them—and a baby! Could it be they were coming to stay? They were.

Squanto, who could speak English well, thanks to his having been kidnaped and his wide travels through Europe, soon discovered that the ship was called the *Mayflower,* and that the people who had landed from her were fleeing from other white people who had been unkind to them. They had come to live where they could worship God as they pleased, without fear of being sent to prison.

Squanto watched as they began to build houses to protect them from the winter. He saw how cold and hungry they were. He saw them grow sick and die.

He knew how many had come off the ship—one hundred and one altogether, plus the baby—but the number, he noticed, got smaller and smaller. Six died before the end of December. Eight died in January, seventeen in February, and thirteen in March. Before spring forty-four of the hundred and one were in their graves, barely three months after the *Mayflower* arrived.

Squanto saw the little processions to the graveyard, the sorrow and the tears of the Pilgrims. After all he had suffered from white men, he could have hated these too and done them great harm. Instead, as one historian has written, "He aided them with a friendship almost beyond understanding."

There was danger that other Indians might attack the Pilgrims and massacre them, but Squanto helped to arrange a treaty with the great chief Massasoit. Knowing both the English and Indian languages, he was just the interpreter the Pilgrims needed.

In his diary Governor Bradford said of Squanto that he di-

Painting by Jennie Brownscombe   Courtesy of Pilgrim Society, Plymouth, Massachusetts

**The Pilgrims invite their Indian friends to the
first Thanksgiving feast and thank God for
their harvest.**

rected them how to set corn, where to fish and to find the other things they needed.

It was Squanto who helped the Pilgrims sow their seed that first spring they were in the New World. He was there, too, in the autumn when their first harvest was reaped and Governor Bradford ordered a three-day feast of thanksgiving.

But for Squanto, there's no knowing what might have happened to the Pilgrims. They might have died of starvation or been killed by hostile Indians. Indeed, the whole course of American history might have been far different but for this one kindhearted Indian who returned good for evil.

◀ Painting by William Heaslip © by Review and Herald

**The Pilgrims were indebted to the Indian
Squanto, who showed them how to plant and
harvest corn, and prepare it for the table.**

37

The Helper Engine

MANY YEARS AGO I was riding in one of the fine express trains that run from San Francisco to Los Angeles in California. The scenery had been quite flat and uninteresting for some time, so that as I sat in my comfortable seat I was gradually becoming more and more sleepy. Then, just before I went to sleep I heard a voice speaking over the public-address system.

"We are approaching the mountains," said the voice. "The train will soon be climbing at the rate of 110 feet every mile. Because one engine is not able to pull the train up so steep a climb, we shall be stopping in a few minutes to take on a helper engine."

By that time, of course, I was wide awake. A helper engine! That sounded so interesting that I wanted to see one.

Very soon the train began to slow to a stop. There was a gentle bump as the helper engine was hooked on for the climb up the mountain.

How easily the train climbed up and up and up! No fuss or bother. In fact, if I hadn't been able to see the mountains from the train window I wouldn't have known we were climbing at all.

As the track wound this way and that, up the steep grade, sometimes almost making a complete circle, I caught brief glimpses of the helper engine. There it was, coupled to the main engine, puffing away in unison with it. That is, when the main engine gave a puff the helper engine gave a puff, and so they went on and up together.

Soon we were over the mountains, and the helper engine was uncoupled. Back it went to help another train up the steep slope.

Then I began to think of all the little engines in people's homes that could be such a help if they would.

"Engines?" you say. "We don't have any engines in our home."

Oh, yes, you do! Big ones and little ones too. One of the big engines, of course, is Daddy, and what a load he has to pull as he toils to earn the money to keep the home together! How hard it must be sometimes to drag the long train of all the family needs—and wants—up the steep mountains of life!

Another engine is called Mother, and how she does have to work to keep the place tidy and do the washing and prepare all the meals and look after the sick folks! What a climb it is for her sometimes!

Then there are the little engines that could be such wonderful helper engines. They have all sorts of names—Billy and Jerry and Molly and Clarice and Helen and Jackie and a host of others.

If they wanted to, you know, they could stand ready at the steep places, with steam all up, ready for service. Then, when they saw Daddy or Mother beginning to get tired under the strain, why, they could hitch right up with them and make their tasks much lighter. Couldn't they now?

I can think of all sorts of ways in which these little helper engines could give the main engines a big strong pull; and no doubt you can think of ways, too.

They could bring in the wood for the fire.

They could wash the dishes—and the kitchen floor sometimes.

They could make the beds too—at least their own.

They could clean the bathtub and the basin.

They could cut the grass or water the flowers.

They could polish the shoes.

They could even do some of the washing and ironing, perhaps.

Oh, there are just a hundred or more ways in which the little helper engines could give the main engines a good hearty pull up the mountains of life—if they would!

Are you a helper engine? I wonder! What does Mother say about it?

STORY **38**

Hoping
Against Hope

WHEN I WAS a boy, one of the things I most wanted to do was to explore the North Pole or the South Pole. Just why, I do not remember. Probably I had read something about the many brave men who have set out on such expeditions. Perhaps, too, I had come under the strange spell of the unknown.

Of course, it was just a boyish dream, and after a time I changed my mind. But others still feel the call of the polar regions and cannot rest till they have seen those great white wastes of snow and ice.

In 1947 Admiral Byrd, who once explored the North Pole, went south, taking with him four thousand men and a good share of the United States Navy, including a submarine. He

carried planes and even a helicopter, besides bulldozers and
motor-driven sleds. This was exploring in a modern way,
without most of the discomforts and worries experienced by
those who set forth on arctic explorations long ago.

One of the most thrilling polar expeditions ever under-
taken was that by Shackleton and his men in the good ship
Endurance. They started from South Georgia Island in the
South Atlantic Ocean on December 5, 1914, just after the
first world war broke out.

Almost from the first everything went against them. The
weather turned bad, and the sea filled with blocks of ice that
jostled one another and banged against the sides of the ship.

Six weeks later the ice closed in, holding the ship fast.
Neither sails, nor engine, nor both together could move her
forward or backward a single yard.

Thus locked in the ice, the *Endurance* drifted with the
ice floe for many months, from January 18 till October 27,
the ice pressing in and piling up all around her. Finally the
awful pressure crushed the stout vessel as though it had been
a matchbox. Fortunately Shackleton and all his men were
able to get off the ship in time, taking with them food, tents,

M. deV. Lee

sledges, and the ship's boats.

Now they found themselves drifting on an ice floe in the midst of the Arctic Ocean, more than three hundred miles from the nearest land. They lived on this ice floe for five and a half months, with the ice groaning and cracking beneath them and blizzards howling around them. How the men endured such hardships, in sub-zero temperatures, I cannot understand. But they had faith in their leader, and hoped against hope that he would bring them to safety at last.

One night, in pitch darkness, the ice actually split under the tent in which Shackleton himself was lying. He jumped up just in time to save himself from falling into the water. In the morning he saw that the piece of ice on which he had been resting was now several yards away across a deep green pool. Another time when the ice split under the camp, one of the party did fall in, all wrapped in his sleeping bag, and was rescued just in time to save him from the jaws of a killer whale.

At last, on April 2, 1916, they were able to launch their three boats, landing six days later on a desolate, uninhabited, ice-covered rock called Elephant Island. Here Shackle-

ton left twenty-two of his men—some too weak and sick to go any farther—and set out with five others to get help.

They took the largest boat—and that only a whaling boat, twenty feet long—and set sail for South Georgia Island, eight hundred miles away, across the wildest sea in the world. Mountainous waves threatened time and again to sink them. Yet, though drenched with the icy water that constantly poured over the sides, with no way to warm themselves, with little to eat and drink, they kept on their way, hoping against hope they would reach their goal at last.

After seventeen days and nights like this, they reached South Georgia, but found themselves on the wrong side of the island, facing icy cliffs and glaciers. Weak and weary though they were, they drew their boat ashore, and three of them started to walk over the snow-covered mountains to the whaling station on the other side. That was another miracle of endurance.

Then began the work of rescue. First the three men who had been left on the south side of South Georgia Island were picked up. Then Shackleton borrowed a ship and set off at full speed to Elephant Island to save the twenty-two men there. But bad weather and pack ice compelled him to turn back, after getting within seventy miles of his goal. It was most disheartening, but he borrowed a stouter vessel and tried again, only to be beaten back when within twenty miles of the island.

Then he borrowed yet another vessel and tried a third time, but failed, because of bad weather, when a hundred miles away.

Yet he did not give up. He loved his men and he knew they were counting on him to rescue them. So he borrowed a fourth ship, and this time, finding the pack ice open, he rushed in and brought them to safety.

All this time, from April 24 till August 30—nearly four and a half months—the twenty-two men on Elephant Island had somehow managed to exist on a freezing spit of sand at the foot of an ice-covered cliff. By piling up boulders from the beach, packing snow in between, then putting the two boats upside down on top, they had made a hut eighteen feet long by nine feet wide by five feet high. There was no window in it, only one small air vent, and here they all lived and slept, cooked and ate, for all that long time! Outside, icy gales raged, while great, thundering waves often flooded the beach.

What heroes these! No beds but the stones beneath them, no food but the flesh of seals and penguins, no water but melted ice—when they could spare the fuel to melt it—no air to breathe but the stench of that crowded hut. Yet they endured. If ever you are tempted to grumble about your home, your bed, your food, think of these men.

And why did they endure? Because they believed in their leader and hoped against hope that he would return. Though he had gone on such a dangerous journey, they felt sure he would come back to rescue them.

In charge of the marooned men was Frank Wild, a faithful and fearless man. Largely because of his constant optimism the whole party kept up their spirits.

"From a fortnight after I had left," wrote Shackleton in his story of the expedition, "Wild would roll up his sleeping bag each day with the remark, 'Get your things ready, boys, the boss may come today.' And sure enough, one day the mist opened and revealed the ship for which they had been waiting and longing and hoping for over four months."

Thus it was hope that saved them. Had they lost hope and become discouraged they could never have held on. They would have quarreled among themselves and become sick and died. But these courageous explorers kept hoping against hope, and deliverance came at last.

So it must be with us. We must never lose heart, never give up hoping. No matter what happens in our life, if we are trying to please God and do right, all will be well with us at last.

Shackleton's journey to save his men reminds me of another great Leader who has gone to plan a rescue. "I go to prepare a place for you," said Jesus. "And if I go . . . , I will come again, and receive you unto Myself; that where I

192   am, there ye may be also." John 14:2, 3.

While He is gone, we have to stay on our "desolate island"; but we must keep up our courage, and ever be looking for His return. Then someday He will come back and take all who have waited for Him, all the boys and girls who truly love Him, to their heavenly home.

We may wonder why He is so long in coming. We may fear that He has forgotten us. But He cannot and will not forget. He loves us too much for that.

Jesus will keep His promise. We can "hope against hope" in Him. He will return for us; and His coming may be sooner than we think. Like Mr. Wild on far-off Elephant Island, let us say with each new morning, "Get your things ready, boys, the Master may come today."